SO YOU WANT
TO BE A DOCTOR

Other titles in this series available
in Perennial Library

So You Want to Be a Nurse
by Alan E. Nourse, M.D.,
with Eleanore Halliday, R.N.

So You Want to Be a Lawyer
by William B. Nourse,
with Alan E. Nourse, M.D.

SO YOU WANT TO BE A DOCTOR

by ALAN E. NOURSE, M.D.

Revised Edition

PERENNIAL LIBRARY

HARPER & ROW, PUBLISHERS

NEW YORK

So You Want to Be a Doctor (revised edition), was originally published by Harper & Row, Publishers, Incorporated, in 1963.

First PERENNIAL LIBRARY edition published 1965 by Harper & Row, Publishers, Incorporated, New York.

LIBRARY OF CONGRESS CATALOG CARD NUMBER: 63-20316
G-P

In Memory of B. C. N.
  who never became what he wanted to be

CONTENTS

A NOTE TO THE READER

FOR THOSE OF YOU who wonder why a new edition of a book has been issued when the original still seems perfectly satisfactory, a few words of explanation may be helpful.

So You Want to Be a Doctor was first written in the winter of 1956 and spring of 1957. During the intervening years the picture of medical education presented in that book has changed in a number of ways. Some of these changes are minor, but others are extremely important to anyone looking forward to a career in medicine. Thus, even in this short time many parts of the original edition of *So You Want to Be a Doctor* have become badly outdated.

What are these changes? First, strange as it may seem, the pattern of medical education has been steadily evolving. Of course, the basic goals of training in medicine remain the same. The need for top-quality physicians who are dedicated to their work will never change very much. But new ways of accomplishing these goals have been appearing year by year. Medical schools are seeking ways to reduce the time a student must spend in basic medical training, a trend just beginning when this book was first written. Again, there has been a steady movement toward more residency and specialty training for doctors after their graduation from medical school. These and other changes must be considered in any up-to-date book about becoming a doctor.

On the other hand, there have been important changes in opportunity for young people who are eager to begin their medical training. Some of these changes are statistical. In this country in 1957 there were four applicants for every medical school seat available. In 1962 there were only two applicants for each seat. This means that any well-qualified premedical student today has a much better chance for admission to medical school than he might have had six years ago. The great wave of World War II and Korean War veterans has come and gone; in the meantime, a number of other more glamorous scientific careers—particularly in chemistry, physics and the aerospace industries—have been giving our medical schools a run for their money. Other careers seem to offer young people equally exciting prospects, while requiring much briefer (and less costly) training. To many promising students the shorter route often appears to be the better.

Fortunately, other changes have come about. It is now possible for young would-be doctors to see for themselves what careers in medicine can be like before they commit themselves, under the auspices of Project MORE, a program designed by the American Academy of General Practice. Further, the Education and Research Fund of the American Medical Association has begun a revolutionary program, resoundingly successful during its first two years, to make funds available to medical students in all stages of training, so that the ever-increasing costs of medical education can be met by any student without undue hardship. These programs, both quite recent, deserve attention.

Again, there has been a change in my own viewpoint since this book was first written. Originally I sought to discourage poor prospects from starting out on the long road to medicine. I now feel this negative approach is not necessary. Quite enough of the road is in view in these pages, I think, to discourage the discourageable without any special effort on my part. Rather, in this rewriting, I have tried to encourage those who have good prospects, and to show more clearly that the goal is indeed worth the gamble for the ones with the energy and ambition to stick it out.

Finally, this revision gives me the rare opportunity to repair some of my own mistakes. Minor inaccuracies which crept into the first edition have been corrected here. Furthermore, letters from many readers have shown me that certain points were not made clear in the original book; as a result, parts have been expanded or completely rewritten. For instance, the surprising numbers of inquiries from girls interested in medicine suggest strongly that too little was said originally about the opportunities for young women in medicine. In this second edition I have taken pains to correct this oversight.

I hope that these revisions will help maintain *So You Want to Be a Doctor* as an up-to-date and useful guide for prospective doctors, so that the book can continue to serve the purpose for which it was written six years ago.

A.E.N.

INTRODUCTION

THIS BOOK IS written for the many young men and women who have finally decided that they want to become doctors of medicine.

There are thousands of you graduating from high school every June, and enrolling in the premedical curriculum in colleges and universities every September. If I were to ask a hundred of you at random just why you think you want to be doctors I would get a hundred different reasons in reply —some good reasons, some bad. But there would be one common denominator. Each of you, for one reason or another, feels quite strongly that medicine is to be your goal. You want above all else to become a doctor.

Yet an amazing number of would-be physicians, just embarking on the long and difficult road that leads to the degree of Doctor of Medicine, have only the vaguest idea of just what, exactly, their study of medicine is going to involve.

These prospective doctors see the years of study that lie ahead of them as a sort of mysterious, hazy blur. They know, of course, that first they will go to college for a period of time (although they aren't quite sure what "premedicine" is or why they have to take it in the first place). They know that they will then go on to medical school—if they're lucky —for another four years, taking courses in anatomy and physiology and other things with long names, and that they will serve an internship in a hospital. They realize that they must invest a long period of time, and a rather frightening amount of money, in order to complete their medical education.

But just as the practice of medicine has always meant something more than "just another way to make a living," so an education in medicine implies something more than the mere completion of certain courses and the reading of certain textbooks.

Certainly something out of the ordinary happens during those years of study to transform an able and wide-awake student into a qualified and capable doctor of medicine.

But what?

It is my hope that this book will tell you what.

In recent years scores of books have been written about doctors and what they do—I've even written one myself—but very little has been written about how they become doctors. A student may see his goal far ahead with perfect clarity, yet find himself floundering or getting lost along the way because he knows so little about the process of getting there.

If you were planning an auto trip from New York to Seattle, you would first obtain a good road map. It wouldn't tell you everything you needed to know about the trip, by any means. Neither would a guidebook describing the places you would see or the stops you would make along the way. Even a talk with a friend who had just completed the trip wouldn't answer all of your questions—but, taken all together, these things would give you some of the information you needed. At least you would know how much gasoline you were going to have to buy and where the more difficult roadblocks were.

The road to medicine doesn't have many maps or guidebooks. The student starting down the road has dozens of questions in his mind for which he cannot find any answers: What comes next? Is it going to be difficult, or easy? Interesting, or dull? Will it be more than I am capable of handling? Or is it something that I can do if I work hard enough at it? What are my chances—really—of eventually getting through?

And even more important questions: Am I going to like it, after all? What is studying medicine actually like? What do I have to know in order to become a doctor?

It is my hope that this book will answer some of those questions.

There are certain facts that a prospective medical student must face squarely from the very start, because they are going to be with him to the end and simply can't be ignored.

One of these facts is that the study of medicine, from the beginning of premedicine on, is not easy.

This may sound like a platitude, and the normal student's reaction is to plant his feet firmly on the ground and say, "I know it won't be easy—but I can do it."

And very possibly you can; the point is not so much whether you can or cannot as whether you really want to. The cost of a medical education, in terms of time, money, and hard work is extremely high. Is it going to be worth the cost, to you? Is the reward going to satisfy you when you have finally achieved it? You can't know this for sure unless you have a clear and honest picture in mind, to start with, of the goal you are aiming for.

Another fact to be faced: The odds are against you when you set medicine as your goal. There are many places where you may fall along the wayside. If you start along this road, you are frankly gambling on getting through. Knowing this, you should understand clearly just how great the odds are. You should understand the gamble.

The first part of this book will be devoted to these things: the goal you are seeking to achieve and the gamble you are taking to get there. But having these things clearly in mind is only the first step along the way. A second portion of the book will deal with "premedicine," the first three to four years of your medical education. What is it? What is it supposed to accomplish? How important are grades during the premedical years? Which courses are important and which are not?

Many of the questions we will discuss will be extremely practical ones. We will devote a chapter to the most important—and most practical—step of all: making application for admission to medical school. We will discuss the cost of your education in medicine and explore some of the ways you can help defray those costs.

Finally, we will consider in some detail the most exciting part of all—the four medical school years and the internship—and we will try to determine what changes come about to transform a medical student into a doctor of medicine.

It is *not* my intention in this book to try to sell you on medicine as a career. I am assuming that you are already sold, or very nearly so. You will find here some of the answers to some of the questions that are already in your mind about how the years of your study of medicine are going to be spent. I won't try to make the road sound easier than it is, but I hope I can show you some of the fun and excitement you will experience along the way. You won't find short cuts here; there aren't any short cuts. Perhaps when you have finished reading you will understand why there can't be. But you will find information here, and perhaps some encouragement when things are looking grim.

My major qualification—perhaps the only one!—for writing this book is the fact that not long ago I too traveled the road you will be traveling. I didn't see everything there was to see along the way, not by any means, but at least I saw where the major roadblocks were. I had a thousand questions which I answered the hard way. I hope that I can answer some of your questions the easy way.

You can use this book in any way you wish. You can read it for fun, interest, or information. You may find it useful for future reference.

If it makes you feel more confident and certain of your decision to become a doctor, and if it makes the trip more pleasant, it will have done its job.

ALAN E. NOURSE, M.D.

SO YOU WANT
TO BE A DOCTOR

ONE

The Goal

IT IS EARLY on a sunny afternoon in June, and you are present at a solemn occasion.

The main graduation ceremonies with the other schools in the university are over, the scholarly procession finished, the honorary degrees awarded, the commencement address completed. Now you are meeting in the medical school auditorium with the rest of your medical school class for your own special ceremony—the goal you have been seeking for so many years.

The auditorium is hushed as the dean of the medical school reads the ancient, dignified words of the Oath of Hippocrates. (You do not recite it, as you had imagined you would, yet the solemn impact of those words comes home to you as you hear them now, and you silently bind yourself to them.) When the oath has been read there is a pause, and then the list of names begins, and you watch your colleagues one by one step up to the stage of the auditorium. You hear your name, see the warm smile of congratulation, and feel the handshake as the stiff gray envelope is placed in your hand.

Your name is engraved on the outside, and below it you see the seal of the university, and the words: DOCTORIS IN ARTE MEDICA.

This, then, is the thing you have waited so long to receive, the diploma which symbolizes the years of work and preparation you have just completed. You have become a member of a vast fraternity, with noble traditions to uphold. There were many times when you thought you would never see this day. There were moments of doubt even up to the very day itself.

But now the worry and doubt are gone. You have reached your goal.

DOCTOR OF MEDICINE

What does it mean?

Not long ago I accompanied a friend of mine who races hydroplanes to inspect the new "thunderboat" which he was going to race on Lake Washington the following week.

It was a beautiful craft: brand-new, low and sleek, painted and polished to perfection. I walked around it in admiration and ran my finger across the shiny hull. Already I could see it flashing over the water, throwing up a rooster tail of spray behind it.

But my friend gave the outside of the boat one perfunctory glance and disappeared inside to examine the motor. First he took a nut off here and a bolt off there. In a matter of twenty minutes he had the entire motor in pieces on the workbench while the mechanic stood by moaning and wringing his hands. Not until the engine was completely dismantled did my friend give an appreciative grunt to indicate that all was to his satisfaction.

"Why did you do that?" I asked him later. "That poor mechanic will have a week's work just putting it back together again!"

"Never mind the poor mechanic," my friend said. "What about me? I'll be taking that thing out on the water at 150 miles an hour. The purse is only $25,000 if I win—but if that motor falls apart it could kill me. I want to *know* what's underneath that paint job before I climb into the thing."

The study of medicine is a far cry from hydroplane racing, but the two things have certain elements in common. You, as a would-be physician, propose to invest nine years of hard work and something on the order of fifteen or twenty thousand dollars in a venture that has many aspects of a gamble. That is a great deal of time and money to risk if you are not sure of the goal that lies ahead.

When you finally receive that hard-earned degree of Doctor of Medicine, what is it really going to mean? What goal will it symbolize? How much of a gamble must you take to achieve it? We ought to be sure what is underneath the paint job before climbing into the boat.

The goal may not be worth the gamble. That is something you will have to decide for yourself. If you believe that it is, no amount of discouragement will turn you aside from trying —but in any event a clear understanding of both the goal and the gamble will remove any lingering doubt from your mind.

The Scope of Medicine: A Thousand Opening Doors

At 3:25 A.M. a doctor in a small midwestern town is awakened by the telephone at his bedside. On a farm ten miles away the young mother of three children has been taken suddenly ill. She is feverish, her frightened husband says. She was awakened by the sudden onset of violent pain in her abdomen, and she is growing rapidly weaker as the pain becomes more severe. Could the doctor come out and see her?

The doctor dresses quickly and arrives at the farm less than half an hour after the call came. The woman is certainly ill; the doctor examines her carefully, noting the rigid abdomen, the pain centered on the left side, the pale, cold skin, the thready pulse. In spite of her pain he gently draws from her a history which means little to her but much to him. He knows half a dozen conditions that could be causing these symptoms, but it seems to him that the most likely diagnosis is a ruptured tubal pregnancy. Thirty years before he might have been forced to perform the necessary surgery in the kitchen of the farmhouse, without assistance and to the great peril of his patient. Now, with modern hospital facilities in the neighboring town and with an experienced anesthetist and a skilled operative assistant, he knows that the damage can be safely repaired. He assures the farmer that his wife will be on her way to recovery in a very few hours. . . .

In a clinic building in a large eastern city a world-famous neurosurgeon steps out of the operating room and goes down to see the family of his patient waiting in his office. "Yes, we found a tumor," he tells the patient's father, "but we can be quite certain that it was not malignant. We were able to remove it completely. Your son should recover quickly, and should never have a recurrence." Unfortunately, the neurosurgeon reflects, he cannot always bring such good news from the operating room—but every year new techniques are perfected, new facts learned, which steadily make his work more fruitful. . . .

In a neighboring large city a doctor sits in an office in the Public Health Department building, conducting a well-baby clinic. Several dozen mothers with their infants are waiting to have their children checked against possible trouble. The baby's growth and development will be discussed. The feeding formula may be altered; infant inoculations will be given. The doctor may spend the entire afternoon without seeing a single sick baby, yet he knows that his work will give these children a better chance to grow up healthy and strong.

In the laboratory of a medical school a young M.D. peers into the incubator at the rows of soil bacteria cultures he is growing there. He does not practice medicine; part of his time is spent teaching medical students bacteriology and the rest is devoted to his own research work with bacteria cultures. He knows that the bacteria on those culture plates produce a powerful new antibiotic agent. Now he must spend weeks and months testing the drug to make sure that it is safe for use in human beings. If it is, there will soon be a new weapon in the modern arsenal of antibiotic weapons against bacterial disease. . . .

In California a young surgeon divides his time between his patients and his work in the physiology laboratory, studying the effects of shock on animals of various types. He recalls vividly the long, hard hours of rushed work in the surgical field unit in Korea not many years before as wounded men in shock were transported in from the battlefield. But the experience in the field in Korea taught him a great deal about the great killer on the battlefield—shock—and how to combat it, and he knows that next time more men will be saved. . . .

In a laboratory somewhere in New Mexico another young physician is studying the effects of cosmic ray bombardment upon living creatures which travel beyond earth's atmospheric blanket into outer space. He is working with the Department of Space Medicine, a bureau of our national government. The primary purpose of this man's work is research to help insure that our future spaceship crews will be able to travel for prolonged periods through interplanetary space and return without medical ill effects. But because of the experience he is accumulating in all aspects of space medicine, it is quite possible that he may be a member of one of the first crews to step from a rocket ship onto the surface of the moon. . . .

Six men, each engaged in totally different types of work, pursuing widely different interests—yet each has one thing in common with all the others. All of them are doctors. All have been over the road you are about to start traveling. All have been awarded the degree of Doctor of Medicine, and all have served their internship year in a hospital.

Yet out of this common educational background has come a wide variety of occupations. The work of the six men I have mentioned can only hint at the vast scope of modern medicine, for the different kinds of work that medicine encompasses are almost unlimited.

The fact is that the study of medicine is the key which can open literally thousands of doors to the graduate physician. You may wish to practice clinical medicine—see patients, treat illness; go into general practice, or go on for training in a clinical specialty such as surgery or pediatrics. If so, the door is open to you when you have completed your basic medical training. Perhaps you will choose to enter a research field either in clinical medicine or in an allied field such as biochemistry or physiology. You may want to combine the practice of medicine with a research program; many physicians do. Or you may find the Public Health Service to be the niche into which you can fit most comfortably.

Whether your interest lies in general medical practice or in surgery, psychiatry or obstetrics, teaching or research, you can find a place in medicine. A thousand doors are open to you; the choice, then, is up to you. Once you have completed the study of medicine in college and medical school and internship you can write your own ticket. In any field of medicine there is room at the top. How far you go and what you accomplish as a physician depends upon how hard you want to work to achieve your position, and for how long.

But the variety of choices is tremendous.

How can it be that medicine, of all the professions, offers so many different opportunities? The answer lies in the basic nature of medicine itself. Throughout the ages medicine has played not one but two roles in our society.

The first, and most obvious, is the care of the sick and injured. Always medicine has been concerned with treating illness and relieving suffering through the use of medications, surgery, and many other forms of treatment. Even the most primitive societies have had their "medical" men—witch doctors and magicians. In our modern world the physician is the guardian of our health and physical welfare.

The second role of medicine is not so tangible, but perhaps even more important than the first: to carry out the search for knowledge about life, to seek a better understanding of the illnesses and afflictions of men and thus to find new ways to combat them. More and more the search has turned toward the prevention of disease, when possible, and the early detection of illnesses at a point where cure is still possible. In this search the final enemy is death, and the goal is life. There could be no broader limits than these extremes, and medicine is concerned with the entire area that lies between them.

This search has been going on since earliest times, but never before in history have we stood so close to the brink of discovery. We have learned more about life and illness and death in the past fifty years than in five thousand years previously. We have developed new techniques; we have found new weapons against disease; we have devised new methods of study.

There has never been a time when medical studies have promised a richer or more exciting reward to those who are beginning the study of medicine, when so many things are almost—but not quite—within our grasp, just waiting for the right man with the right idea and enough energy and courage to carry it through to come along.

This is the challenge medicine can offer you. You will find excitement here—the excitement of contributing to a great era of medical discovery. There is much work to be done; many barriers must be crossed, but for the first time in history there seems now to be a good chance that we may eventually win.

Rewards and Responsibilities

A modern physician can, of course, look forward to certain tangible rewards for his work in medicine. Doctors, by and large, make good livings from their work. It would be pointless to list average incomes of doctors in the various specialties as they are today because those incomes may be quite different by the time you have finished with your medical training. However, as one cynical acquaintance of mine recently pointed out, you would have to look for a long time to find a doctor who is starving to death.

Certainly a physician has a high degree of financial security. He can always find work. He can reasonably expect to have a home of his own and a good automobile. He can expect to be able to afford a summer home, perhaps, or to travel during his vacation time. He will be able to provide a good education for his children.

On the other hand, it would be a mistake to expect to make a great deal of money from the practice of medicine. There are physicians who do, of course, but they are the exceptions. There are other fields of endeavor in which you can make much more money with much less effort, if that is your major concern.

Aside from income, there are other rewards for a physician. He will enjoy respect in his community. No other position is held in as high regard as the profession of medicine. The doctor is respected merely for being a doctor. He is regarded to some degree as "community property" and is often a leader in community progress and a consultant in completely non-medical community affairs.

Most important, the physician derives immense satisfaction from doing work that is worthwhile, work which is needed and received with gratitude and respect. He finds satisfaction in doing work which comparatively few others can do, and doing it well. He can see every day the positive benefit that comes from his work.

These rewards will be yours when you enter the medical profession, but you must at the same time assume certain unusual responsibilities. Very often patients tend to forget that their doctors are people as well as doctors. A doctor is expected to be available when he is needed. If that happens to be at three in the morning, it is still his responsibility to answer the call. Very often the physician works hours that would horrify the average businessman—not as an unusual occurrence, but as his normal way of life.

During my internship I once computed that I was working 125 hours a week, and was feeling very sorry for myself, until a weary general practitioner of my acquaintance pointed out that he was working 130 hours a week. And internship was supposed to be the time of the longest hours and the hardest work!

The doctor's home life is often a very sketchy proposition, especially during the years when he is establishing his practice. He has little time at home. It has been said that any woman who marries a doctor is either an idiot or a fool; if this is so, I know quite a number of very charming idiots and fools who are willing to share their husbands, rather unequally, with the many demands of a medical practice, duties that take the doctor away from home "usually half the night and always at mealtimes."

This demand upon the doctor's time is unavoidable, and is accepted by the profession as part of the game. It is the way a doctor lives, and that is all there is to it. Doctors usually feel that if someone doesn't care for that kind of life he shouldn't be a doctor, and there is no one whom the profession scorns more than the physician who shirks his responsibilities, places his personal life above his duties, and refuses to regard his time as public property. The rest of the profession accepts its responsibilities—why shouldn't he?

It is true, of course, that in recent years many doctors have formed "group practices," practicing medicine in partnership, with one doctor in a group covering calls for another when he is off duty. By the time you are doctors the single practitioner working twenty hours a day may well be a thing of the past. But your responsibility to your patients, on duty or off, will never change.

"Keeping Up with Medicine": A Lifetime Job

We are dealing in this book with the years of formal medical education—college, medical school, internship. But a doctor's education is not completed when he finishes his internship and receives his license to practice medicine. In fact, it has barely begun.

As a physician, you will be committed to a lifetime of study. Every patient you see will teach you more medicine. You will continually learn from your colleagues in practice, and from seminars and conferences that you will attend. There will be medical journals and textbooks to read. You will be faced with the problem of keeping up to date in medicine. With the rate of progress we have seen in recent years this can be a formidable task indeed.

Every physician faces a dilemma: It is utterly impossible for one person in his lifetime to learn more than a small fraction of what he needs to know to be a good physician—and yet when the first patient walks into his office he is expected and morally bound to know everything there is to be known about medicine in order to give that patient the best medical care possible.

There is no solution to the problem; the doctor does the best he is equipped to do. But he can never sit back with folded hands and be content only with what he has already learned. He must constantly labor to learn more. The article he reads in the new medical journal one day may save the life of a patient the day after.

Doctors know this, and accept it, and would not have it any other way. The deeper you penetrate its mysteries, the more fascinating medicine becomes in all of its facets: research, discovery, diagnosis, care, and treatment. Medicine is a challenge. It carries great rewards and great responsibilities. Doctors do not give their time and energy grudgingly—the work is far too interesting, too absorbing and engrossing.

And they know that there is too much to be learned, and too little time to learn it.

TWO

The Gamble

THIS, THEN, is the goal toward which you have taken your first step when you decide that you want to be a doctor. I realize that the description is incomplete and inadequate. Each one of you will discover something different in medicine. What is more, as you learn more about your profession, your ideas about what you want from medicine as a career will change. You may be starting off with the conviction that you want to be a surgeon, and not discover until your third year of medical school that you really don't like surgery at all and would prefer to study pediatrics and become a "baby doctor." Perhaps you will maintain your interest in general practice throughout medical school—but you may become involved in a research project that is so interesting that you discard your idea of practicing medicine altogether. Or you may discover, to your surprise, that of all fields of medicine psychiatry is to you the most exciting.

And this is perfectly all right; pediatricians are useful people to have around, and psychiatrists are badly needed. Your medical training will give you firsthand experience in all branches of medicine. It would be foolish to make up your mind too firmly until you have a chance to see as many of the possibilities as you can.

But whatever position you seek to achieve in the medical profession, first you must satisfy the basic educational standards required of all physicians. The common denominator of all medical work is a basic medical education leading to the degree of Doctor of Medicine. To the would-be doctor just beginning premedicine in college this represents a gamble, with the odds stacked against him in many ways.

What Is the Gamble?

When you begin your training for medicine, you must be prepared to invest at least nine years of your life and (as of 1963) somewhere between fifteen and twenty thousand dollars of your money on the chance that you will be able to achieve your goal.

The nine years is actually a minimum. Although it is true that some medical schools will accept candidates for admission who have completed only three years of college, and that others are trying to reduce the time in training by combining part of premedical training with medical school, the fact remains that most students will finish college and take a bachelor's degree before entering medical school. After four years of college, another four years will be spent in medical school, and a minimum of one year must be completed as an intern in a teaching hospital before you will be eligible for a license to practice medicine.

Very few modern doctors stop with this nine-year minimum, however. Even though they are free at that point to take licensure examinations and start out into general practice, more and more young doctors feel that their training is still incomplete when they have finished internship. Those who are interested in practicing general medicine may then take one or more years of general medical residency in a hospital. In order to enter specialty practice—internal medicine, surgery, obstetrics, radiology—as much as three to five years of advanced residency training may be required, and sometimes even more. Thus the total time investment may be as high as twelve to fourteen years of study after high school, and could be even longer.

Of course doctors in their residencies in hospitals receive some remuneration for their services, but the feeling seems to be that the hospital work will be done much better if the interns and residents are kept slightly hungry while they are doing it. The stipends are rarely generous. An intern may be paid as much as twenty cents an hour for the time he is on duty, a resident perhaps thirty cents an hour. Even though the trend is toward more realistic stipends for doctors in this advanced stage of their training, there are still many hospitals which pay their interns nothing at all except room and board, and provide their residents with twenty-five dollars a month for spending money. These hospitals contend that interns and residents are receiving invaluable training in return for their services, and feel that that should be reward enough.

In any event, you will be investing at least nine years, and possibly twelve or more, in pursuing your medical education. It is significant that these are the years occurring between the ages of eighteen and thirty-five for most students—the years during which your high school classmates will be establishing themselves in business, or law, or in whatever other field they may have chosen. A close friend of mine in college was a mathematics major who graduated a year after I did. I went on to medical school while he looked for a job. Five years later he had become an expert in the field of electronic computers and was drawing a salary of twelve thousand dollars a year, while I was an expert in very little, with far more liabilities than assets on my record book.

As for the cost of medical training, fifteen thousand dollars is the roughest of rough estimates, but it seems unlikely that a student starting today could get by for much less. Here a great deal depends upon where you go to college, how much scholarship assistance you can obtain and which medical school you attend. You may pay far less for your premedical training at your own state-supported university than at a private college or university. This is also true, to a much smaller degree, in many state-supported medical schools, but here the tuition fees are likely to be quite high even for residents of the state. In college the cost depends to some extent upon how expensive your tastes are—but in medical school the costs level off pretty much. Everyone has the same expenses, and they all are high.

Quite aside from tuition, fees, and books you must also consider the cost of your food and lodging as part of your educational expenses. Some students are able to minimize these costs by living at home, but the majority must pay them out of their own pockets.

In any event, fifteen thousand dollars is a conservative estimate of the cost of medical education computed according to costs as they are now. This is money that you will have to provide during the course of the nine years, one way or another. You will not necessarily have to have the money in the bank before you begin, but it will have to come from somewhere sometime during the nine years. Strange as it may seem, you will still be getting off very cheaply indeed at that figure, for most medical schools run in the red, and no medical school in the country could continue to train doctors if it relied solely on tuition and fees from its students.

In later chapters we will discuss some of the ways in which all that money can be raised, including a new student loan program which recently has made the way immensely easier for thousands of would-be doctors with limited funds. But it's worthwhile to take a long look at those figures before we go on. Fifteen thousand dollars is a lot of money. It's enough to buy a home to live in for the rest of your life. It's enough to set you up in business. You will need it, ironically enough, at precisely the time when you are least able to provide it. You owe it to yourself to be sure that you are spending the money in the wisest way possible before you invest it in a medical education.

Why Does It Take So Long?

This is one of the most frequent questions asked about medical education, and it is not a surprising question. After all, nine years is a long time to study for a profession. Four years of college seems ample preparation for many fields of work. A lawyer can prepare for his profession with two years of college and three years of law school. Why does it take so long to prepare a doctor for his work?

The United States government asked exactly the same question during World War II, when the country was faced with the most severe shortage of physicians in its history. The government decided that it shouldn't take so long, and set out to do something about it.

Men were admitted to medical schools in large numbers after only three years of premedical training, and the medical schools cooperated with accelerated year-round programs to cram four years of medical training into three. It worked, within limits. This accelerated program produced a great many doctors quickly—and good doctors, too. Many of the men trained under the wartime program are leading men in their medical fields today.

But something was missing.

The accelerated program taught the facts and techniques of medicine, true. It taught the students biochemistry and anatomy, pathology and diagnosis. But it did not teach them to be doctors.

That they had to learn the hard way, by themselves, in the years after their formal medical training was completed.

Unlike mathematics, or physics, or business administration, the study of medicine is not primarily a study of facts, methods, and techniques. The facts are important, of course, but something else is far more important. The prospective doctor must learn a whole new method of thinking. He must learn observation—not by learning that he should look for this, and this, and this when he sees a patient, but by actually observing hundreds of patients, and learning what experienced physicians have observed about them, and comparing this with what he has observed. The would-be doctor must understand people and how they behave, not according to what the rulebook says, but by the experience of dealing with them, sick and well, over months and years. He must learn techniques of detection that would make a police inspector blush with envy . . . not by studying detection as a science, but by the long process of ferreting out diagnoses by trial and error with hundreds of patients in hospital wards.

On top of all this, he must have time to grow, time to think, and time to mature. He must have time to let a multitude of rich medical-school experiences soak in and become a part of his thinking. He must have time to gather together loose ends. It is this vague, intangible part of medical education that makes the difference between learning to go through the motions of being a doctor and learning medicine. Medicine is a science in many respects, but it is also an art. In studying medicine there is no substitute for time and experience. It is not so much what you learn in medical school that counts as what you absorb and make a part of your everyday thinking.

This process of absorbing will have begun long before you enter medical school. You have already begun it. Many students are impatient with the college preparation required by medical schools. They want to get into the meat of medicine, and can't see the value of "wasting" three or four years in college.

But, as we will see, the college years are just as essential to a sound medical education as the medical school years. You can't afford to slight them and hope to become a good doctor.

A Look at the Odds

A gambler always wants to know the odds against him before he begins his gamble. Certainly if you are thinking of risking the time and money required for a medical education you should have some idea of the odds against your getting through. You have heard that certain of the premedical courses are man-killers and that many students fail to gain admission to medical school. You have heard, perhaps, that many students who are admitted to medical school flunk out during the first year. What, then, are the odds against you?

Statistically, the odds are pretty high.

We do not know exactly how many students enter as freshman premedical students in American colleges and universities each year. We do know, however, that approximately fifteen thousand premedical seniors are now applying for admission to medical schools each year. It is safe to assume that from three to four times that many students start college each year with medicine in mind.

We also know that each year approximately seventy-five hundred men and women are awarded the degree of Doctor of Medicine from accredited American medical schools.

Obviously there is considerable "mortality" somewhere along the line. Not as many fall by the wayside now as was once the case. In the years after World War II there were many more applicants to medical school than there were places; four or five students competed for each available freshman seat. But even today there are at least two applicants for each place, and still more turn aside even before they have completed premedicine in college.

Of course, these are only statistics—merely numbers on the balance sheet. You are individuals, not statistics. Some of you may actually have a 95 per cent chance of going straight through premedicine and medical school without a hitch. Others of you may not even stand a 5 per cent chance.

But on the balance sheet, probably only one out of eight or ten students starting toward medicine will actually achieve the goal.

This emphatically does not mean that all the rest necessarily are going to flunk out somewhere along the line. It simply means that for one reason or another all the rest will ultimately fail to become doctors.

Then, what happens to them?

During my service in the Hospital Corps of the United States Navy, before I started my premedical work in college, I had three good friends who were, like me, determined to become doctors.

All three of these men were intelligent and capable. We had all chosen the Hospital Corps of the Navy because of our interest in medicine. All of us left service to enter freshman premedical courses with our shared goal—a medical degree—clearly in sight.

Bill finished one year and no more. He had been married while he was in the Navy, and had a baby daughter when he started college. During his freshman year another baby came. His family could not help very much with the financial burden of his education. Today, Bill might have squeezed by with the financial help that is available for medical students . . . but at that time, for him, the gamble was too great. He left college, and is now running a business of his own, with a healthy, happy son and daughter and a good income.

But he didn't become a doctor.

With Dean it was a different story entirely. He had the funds to carry him through, and started off in premedicine with enthusiasm. Because the college he attended happened to have an excellent psychology department, Dean took many of his elective courses in psychology. The more he worked in that field the more he liked it, and the less interested he became in going on with medicine. By the time he was a senior in college it was obvious that for him medical school would be a mistake. He had found another field of work which was far more interesting to him. After college he spent several years as a juvenile probation officer in a city in the Pacific Northwest, and now is happy and excited about his new position as director of a large juvenile rehabilitation program in Southern California. He has never regretted his decision to change over from premedicine to psychology—but he did not become a doctor.

The third man's experience was not so happy. Mac finished premedicine with an average scholastic record and had perfectly acceptable recommendations when he made application to medical school—but he was not admitted. He took another year of work at his university, earning a master's degree in chemistry, but still he was not admitted to a medical school. There was no single specific thing which barred him. He had no black marks against him; his grades, although not outstanding, were at least adequate to meet medical school requirements. But he still was refused admission.

Mac had run up against the solid, if unhappy, fact that there simply are not enough seats in this country's medical schools to accommodate everyone who applies. Every year highly qualified students lose out. It may seem unfair; there may be no logical reason for it in any given case, and medicine undoubtedly loses some fine doctors every year because of it, but the fact remains. Mac took a job with a manufacturer of hospital equipment, and the last I heard he was directing the construction of a 700-bed hospital in Venezuela. He joined the ranks of those who wanted to be doctors and lost out through no fault of their own. To him it was a bitter disappointment. He had the desire and the qualifications—but he did not become a doctor.

Of course, there are many who just can't make the grade. Some fail in one of the critical premedical courses. Others perhaps have no failures but find that their overall college average is just not good enough to meet the competition.

But it is also true that interests and ambitions can change. Many prospective doctors change their minds along the way.

Even in medical school occasional students drop out volun-
tarily, in spite of good grades and the high regard of their
professors, because they have discovered at that late date that
medicine is not for them.

Unfortunately, until very recently there was no really good
way that you could judge, from actual contact with doctors at
work, whether you would like the life of a doctor or not. But
now, thanks to a program devised by the American Academy
of General Practice, opportunities can be made for high
school students interested in medical careers to observe and
learn about the life of a doctor firsthand in their own commu-
nities. Project MORE was first tested in 1961 in high schools
in Binghamton, New York and Omaha, Nebraska. Local physicians met with interested students to describe from their
own experiences what careers in medicine could be like. Then
students who were seriously interested were invited to
"shadow" their doctor-preceptors for a day, interviewing patients, making hospital rounds and house calls . . . even observing operating-room procedures, with the doctors ready
and eager to answer any questions about medicine that came
their way.

Project MORE was so popular in its first trials that the
program has been growing by leaps and bounds ever since.
As of this writing the American Academy of General Practice
has sponsored Project MORE programs in cities in fifteen
states; plans are under way to extend the program to every
state in the union. If you have not heard of such a program in
your community, write to Project MORE, c/o The American Academy of General Practice, Volker Boulevard at Brook-
side, Kansas City 12, Missouri—or ask your family doctor
how such a program could be arranged in your own community.

For the students who are convinced that they want to be
doctors, there is no need to be discouraged by the odds.
Much depends upon you—what kind of work you do in college, what sort of record you present to the medical school
board of admissions. But you should realize that you may fail
to make the grade at one point or another. Other interests
may appear as new doors open to you during your college

years. You should not close your mind to any other possibilities simply because you have found an interest in medicine. This would be like walking through the world with blinders on, and your four years of college are far too exciting for that.

THREE

Premedicine:
The Requirements

LET'S ASSUME that you have given your ultimate goal—a career in medicine—another long look. You have considered the gamble you must take, as objectively as possible; you recognize the odds you are facing, and you have found that your original decision still holds firm. You want to become a doctor.

That decision, intelligently and honestly made with all the cards on the table, is your first big step on the road toward your goal. You have enrolled in the premedical section of an accredited college or university, prepared to work hard for that goal. Now you are facing the second step: the completion of a period of premedical training which you hope will culminate in your admittance to a medical school.

To all intents and purposes this means that you must complete four years of college and earn a bachelor's degree in either arts or sciences.

Not so many years ago premedical training was not considered so important to a doctor's education as it is today. Medical schools routinely accepted students who had finished only three years of college—sometimes only two years. Unfortunately for the impatient student who burns to be in medical school, this is no longer the case.

While medical schools will still occasionally accept certain students after only three years of premedical training, this practice is now the exception rather than the rule. Most schools specify that only the most exceptional applicants will be considered for admission under these circumstances, and the actual admission figures in recent years bear out this claim.

So, in planning your premedical years, it would be wise to count on four years of college work before medical school. You may wish to apply for admission to the school of your choice after only three years, but your chances for admission at that point will be slender. Regardless of medical school policies, and in spite of certain recent experimental programs seeking to shorten the total period of medical training, the fact remains that four years of college premedical work is still the ideal preparation for a would-be doctor, and the medical schools know it. It is the preparation that will give you the best chance for acceptance in a medical school class when the time comes.

Why is this so? What, exactly, *is* premedicine? What are you expected to learn during those four years that makes this initial part of your medical training too important to be slighted? What are you expected to accomplish?

Premedicine Has a Purpose

These are questions asked by many prospective medical students who are eager to get into the thick of their medical studies. To many, premedicine seems to be a needless delay, a useless barrier that is standing in their way. After all, they say, premedicine consumes time and money—and for what?

Unfortunately, we can't give a pat all-inclusive answer. But suppose you were able to skip premedicine altogether and move directly from your high school graduation into the first year of medical school. How well do you think you would manage?

The sad truth is that you almost certainly would fail. You might well be the brightest and most capable of all high school graduates—but you wouldn't last a year in medical school. You wouldn't be able to handle the load of work required of you. You wouldn't be able to compete with your classmates. You wouldn't really understand much of anything that was going on around you in lectures and laboratories, and unless you were really a genius-level student you probably wouldn't be able to learn fast enough to save yourself.

You would simply take a resounding bellyflop, and very probably would never quite understand what hit you.

Yet with four years of college premedical work behind you, you might well have had an excellent chance of holding your own in medical school and taking your M.D., and might have become an excellent doctor.

Premedicine has a purpose. It isn't imposed upon a student as a prerequisite for medical school simply because of its annoyance value. Its purpose is obvious, and yet many prospective medical students fail to see this.

The purpose of premedicine is to prepare you for the study of medicine.

In this chapter and the chapters following we will discuss just what this preparation consists of, and how it is accomplished. Part of it is the fulfillment of flat requirements, laid down by the medical schools for very sound reasons, as we will see. Part of it is the elective courses you will take and the new fields of learning you will explore in them. Part of it is the extracurricular life you will lead while you are at college.

None of it is unimportant; every part of it dovetails into the process of education and training which will slowly but surely change you from a student of medicine into a capable physician.

The Requirements Are the Thing

Many students in premedicine consider that they have but one all-important objective from the first day they enter college as a member of a premedical class: acceptance by a medical school four years later.

After all, they argue, this is the single greatest hurdle that stands between them and their goal. If at the end of premedicine they are not accepted into medical school, that is the end of their sojourn in medicine.

To a certain degree, these students are right. Gaining admittance to medical school is not by any means the only objective of premedicine, as we will see, but certainly it is a matter of critical importance to the would-be physician. And it is never, in any way, an automatic thing. Even the finest scholastic record in premedicine cannot be considered a guarantee of acceptance into medical school.

Since acceptance by a medical school is so important, our consideration of what premedicine is supposed to accomplish might best begin with the medical schools themselves.

What do the powers-that-be in medical school look for in an applicant for admission? What do they want to see in their prospective medical students?

In short, what do they expect premedical training to accomplish?

Every medical school has a group of men and women chosen from its faculty which acts as a board of admissions to consider each applicant for admission. In most cases this board consists of the dean of the medical school, his assistant, and members from several departments—some physicians, some not. Each application for admission is reviewed by this board with a single all-important question in mind: Is this student likely to become a good doctor?

If the members feel, on the basis of all the information they have about a student, that the answer is yes, that student will very probably be admitted to the freshman class. If the answer is no, for whatever reason, the student will receive an unhappy message in the mail, regretfully informing him that his application has not been accepted.

But, you may ask, how can this group of people tell whether you will be a good doctor or not? On what do they base their decision? What are their criteria?

Every medical school board of admissions in the country will ask approximately the same questions in considering the application of a premedical student:

1. Has he completed at least the minimum of scholastic work that we require? Has he taken the courses we prescribe for premedical training? What grades has he received? Has he had any failures? Are his grades particularly outstanding, or just ordinary?

2. At what college or university has he studied? What is its scholastic standing? How have students from that school done in our medical school in the past?

3. What kind of recommendations has he earned from his

college professors—particularly those teaching scientific courses? Do they think he will be a good doctor?

4. How well rounded is his education? Has he demonstrated an interest in anything besides science? Is he good at anything else? Is his educational background broad, or is it narrow and restricted?

5. What were his results in the Medical College Admission Test he took during his junior year of college?

6. What sort of person is he? Is he a leader or a follower? What were his extracurricular activities in college? What about his hobbies and outside interests? Is he honest? Trustworthy? Capable of assuming responsibility? Dependable? In short, is he the sort of person that a doctor ought to be?

7. How did he impress us when we interviewed him? Did we like him? Did he strike us as being "doctor material"?

8. How does he compare with other applicants we are considering? With more applicants than freshman-class seats available, will we have to turn away more promising individuals if we accept this student?

9. How does he plan to finance the cost of medical school? Will he be able to carry his share of the load, as far as he can foresee?

These, then, are the questions that will be asked about you when you apply for admission to medical school. Grades and courses in premedicine are important, of course, but you can see that many other things are considered equally important, if not more so.

We will discuss grades and courses in the following pages; but we will also consider some of the more intangible factors that play an important part in your premedical training, and indeed in your whole medical education.

The Scholastic Requirements

Every year the Association of American Medical Colleges publishes a pamphlet entitled, "Admission Requirements of American Medical Colleges."

Your college library has a copy of this pamphlet on its shelves, and every premedical student should become acquainted with it. It contains, in brief outline form, the admission requirements of every medical school in the country.

At first glance it may seem to you that the medical schools require so many different courses for admission that you will not have time to do anything else in college. Nothing could be further from the truth. In fact, you will have surprising freedom of choice in the courses you take, particularly in your last two years of college.

However, there are certain courses you will be required to take, and a few of those are of critical importance in your preparation for medical school.

All these required courses have a double purpose. First, they are designed to give you a certain amount of information you will need, to provide you with a scientific groundwork for the medical studies that will come later—a set of working tools which you will use for the rest of your professional life.

But these courses do more than teach you facts. They are also designed to teach you how to study. These are not courses that you will breeze through with ease. It will require hard work to complete them. What is more, if your work is not acceptable in these courses, they may spell the difference between admittance and nonadmittance to medical school.

You will have two sets of scholastic requirements to fulfill: the requirements of your college for a bachelor's degree and the requirements of the medical schools for entrance. The medical school scholastic requirements are the more restrictive, so we will consider these requirements primarily.

Although each individual medical school has its own requirements, the basic requirements are the same in all medical schools. The pamphlet mentioned above will give you the specific details for any medical school in which you are interested. Listed below are the requirements outlined by the Board of Admissions of the University of Pennsylvania School of Medicine in the current Bulletin. These requirements are generally representative of all medical schools in the country:

1. BIOLOGY: One college year. This must include some basic work in both botany and zoology, the study of plant and animal life, and should not be exclusively one or the other. The University of Pennsylvania specifies that the stu-

dent should not take bacteriology or histology as part of the biology requirement, since these are courses given in medical school. You may wish to take these courses in college, but the work will not count as part of the required year of work. (Other medical schools may not have this restriction.)

2. CHEMISTRY: Three college years minimum. This must include inorganic chemistry, analytical chemistry, and organic chemistry; physical chemistry is strongly recommended in addition, but is not required.

3. PHYSICS: One college year minimum, with more recommended if possible.

4. MATHEMATICS: One college year minimum.

5. ENGLISH: Two college years minimum. One of these years may be fulfilled by courses in philosophy or logic rather than in straight English or literature courses.

6. FOREIGN LANGUAGES: Two college years. These should be spent in the study of French, German, or Spanish.

If we figure out these requirements in terms of credit hours of work, we will see that they comprise approximately three-fifths of the minimum total credit hours required for your graduation with a degree. That is, these medical school scholastic requirements consume between 70 and 75 credit hours of college work, while the minimum number of credit hours required for graduation is approximately 126, or 32 per year for four years.

Thus we can see that a student could conceivably cram the work required for medical school admission into three years, but he would have little room left over for anything else.

Actually, you may take considerably more than the minimum 126 credit hours of work. To fulfill college degree requirements you will select a major field of specialization and a minor field of specialization. Most premedical students major in a scientific field—chemistry, for instance, or biological sciences—and take minor work in such a field as history, sociology, or psychology.

This does not mean that you must major in a scientific field. Virtually any major field will be acceptable to a medical school board of admissions as long as you complete the required credit hours in the required courses. But it is up to you to see that you have fulfilled the requirements of the medical school of your choice.

Why Are the Required Courses Required?

This question is asked again and again by premedical students. "I can see the chemistry and biology," you may say, "but why English? I can already read and write. And how will two years of college Spanish help make me a better doctor?"

With English the answer is simple. As a doctor you will need it and need it badly. Being able to read and write is not enough. You must be able to read rapidly and write well.

One of the physician's greatest problems is communicating with his patients. He must be able to understand what they are trying to tell him, no matter how poorly they may speak. Otherwise he cannot hope to diagnose their trouble, much less treat it effectively. He must be skillful in the use of English, for his patient may not be.

The first patient I was called upon to see as a medical student was a lady in the medical ward of the Hospital of the University of Pennsylvania. My job was to take her medical history and record it in a form that my instructor would accept. The lady was in pain, a fact she conveyed to me in a rapid-fire barrage of Italian. It seemed that she didn't speak English too well. In fact, she didn't speak it at all; her entire English vocabulary consisted of "Oh, doctor!" and "It's-a-hurt!"

Since I knew even less Italian than she knew English, the task of taking a history seemed impossible. I spent hours with that woman, using every trick of communication I could devise. We ended up drawing each other elaborate pictures—but I got my medical history before morning rounds began.

Written English is just as important to a doctor as spoken English. A doctor learns by reading. He must be able to communicate his findings to other doctors by writing. During medical school and internship you will write literally millions of words of medical history and physical examination findings, longhand, seeking to say everything of importance as briefly as you can. What you write will become part of the permanent hospital record of your patients, of great importance for future reference.

A clumsy command of English will be a continual stumbling block.

And while we are speaking of English—how well do you read? You will be expected to do a great deal of reading in the next nine years, and to absorb a great deal of what you read. The ability to read fast and comprehensibly will be an almost unbelievable advantage to you, for it will save you days and weeks of precious reading time when you need it most.

Unfortunately, by the time you start premedicine, you will have been reading quite long enough to have some deeply entrenched bad reading habits. I can think of no course in college less inspiring than a course in remedial reading, and I'm sure you can't either, but if your college offers such a course, take it, even if you fancy yourself a fast and accurate reader. It will pay rich dividends in the rest of your college and medical school work.

But what about foreign languages? Why should they be part of the required preparation for medical school?

Here the reason is not quite so simple as in the case of English. First, there is the traditional idea that a person is not really educated unless he has a speaking and reading knowledge of some major language other than his native tongue.

But mostly a foreign language is required because it represents a study discipline. To master the fundamentals of a new language you must work at it, on a regular day-to-day basis over a prolonged period of time. It isn't a question of needing the language for itself; American doctors no longer go to Vienna to complete their medical education (quite the opposite, in fact!) and most important papers in foreign-language journals are available in English translation. It is a question of exposing you to some practice in the art of studying.

Another reason for foreign-language requirements seems valid to me, even if the medical schools might object: You need the practice of assimilating a new language because in medical school you will have to learn still another new language, the language of medical jargon. Contrary to popular belief, the "doctor's language" is not used in order to confuse the patient. It is used because it describes things accurately—to doctors—and saves the doctor much time and many words. But medical jargon is, in a sense, a "foreign language" which you will learn to use. Learning a major European language in college may do much to prepare you for it.

Mathematics is a highly practical requirement. Laboratory work means calculation; it means the use of formulae, of logarithms, of algebra, sometimes of calculus. The deeper you become involved in research or experimental medicine the more you need math as a working tool. College is your last chance to acquire that tool.

No one will argue very much about the requirements for courses in biology. By definition "the study of life," biology covers a lot of territory. It will give you a background you will constantly need, for a physician is in every sense involved in "the study of life."

Much of the material you will encounter in college biology courses will be at least partly familiar to you, old friends in new clothing. You will learn the reasons for things you always took for granted. You will have your formal introduction to the use of the clinical microscope, and your initiation into dissecting. Biology has an obvious application to medicine, and anyone who looks forward to the study of medicine will almost automatically like the courses in biology.

Chemistry and Physics:
The Man-Killers of Premedicine

Although no statistics have been compiled, there is no question that two specific courses account for a higher mortality among premedical students than all the other required courses put together. These courses are first-year physics and organic chemistry. They are the man-killers of premedicine, and they are required as prerequisites by virtually every medical school in the country.

Why are these courses so difficult? For one thing, colleges deliberately make them difficult. Physics and organic chemistry are considered the major "conditioning courses" for medical school. They are difficult studies in themselves. They are loaded with new ideas and concepts; they require careful, logical thinking to master them.

In short, they represent discipline for the student. You will have to buckle down and work to master these courses. You will be forced to control your study time, for you will be working against the clock in both classroom and laboratory. If you fall a week behind in your work, you risk never catching up again; hence, you discipline yourself to be certain that you don't fall behind.

Both chemistry and physics have much in common with high-school geometry. They are "exact sciences"; a great deal is known about them, and what is known can be proved by repeatable experiment. Chemical reactions work in certain ways under certain conditions for certain reasons, and under no other circumstances.

In both fields there are many facts to be absorbed, not just for the sake of learning facts, but because you will need them for your understanding of sickness and health, diagnosis and treatment.

In chemistry you will learn to follow a chain of logical reasoning in regard to chemical substances and their reactions. In your first year you will learn about "inorganic" materials—substances that do not contain carbon. In analytical chemistry you will learn more about chemical reactions in a form of scientific detective work, learning to identify substances by their peculiar properties. Here you will be introduced to some very specialized laboratory techniques, many of which are the basic tools in any research laboratory.

Finally you will study organic chemistry, the chemistry of carbon and its compounds. This is truly the chemistry of life, since all life on our planet is carbon-based.

Much of your work in chemistry may seem remote from medicine. Actually, it is not. Consider the concept of pH, for example. First you learn that pH is a term having something to do with acids and alkalis. Soon you discover that it is not something arbitrary that was dreamed up to annoy college students, but is actually a description of certain specific properties of solutions. Later you discover that the acidity or alkalinity of a solution depends, in fact, on the presence or absence of hydrogen ions in solution, and that pH is a way of stating the exact, measurable concentration of hydrogen ions present. To be accurate, pH is the negative logarithm of the hydrogen ion concentration, which can be measured to ten decimal places if necessary (math again, you see).

But what does this have to do with medicine? A great deal. In medical school you will learn that the solution of chemical compounds in tissue fluid and blood must be maintained at a very rigid pH level at any cost, or the living creature will die. If you breathe deeply and rapidly for a short period of time— "hyperventilate," to use the medical term—you will soon become aware of a number of uncomfortable sensations. You will begin to feel lightheaded and faint; your fingers will begin to tingle, and presently your muscles will begin to jerk uncontrollably. You are breathing out enough carbon dioxide to raise the pH of your blood a tiny fraction above safe limits, and the physiological reaction is rapid and extreme. Under certain circumstances it could be dangerous, or even fatal.

The point of all this is not to teach you about pH, but to point out how your groundwork in chemistry leads directly to an understanding of illness and health. You are forging tools here that you will constantly use. In a very real sense, you are already digging into the meat of medicine.

At the same time you are learning how to study a complex field of knowledge and master it. You are meeting—perhaps for the first time—the sheer necessity of sitting down over a book and a scratch pad night after night and spending hours getting yesterday's lesson straight so you'll be ready for tomorrow's. You will spend many hours over book and scratch pad before you take your M.D. degree. The sooner you learn how the better.

On the other hand, if you can't learn to do it—or won't learn—your courses in physics and chemistry will very effectively keep you out of medical school. There are many fields of work that are less demanding; but if medicine is your goal, these courses will be your trial by fire, to see if you are ready for the kind of study discipline you will need in medical school.

This is the case throughout your premedical training. You

learn facts, yes. But more than facts you learn methods of study. You learn to concentrate; in many ways you learn to think.

Most important of all, you learn to ask questions, and to wonder why things are as they are badly enough to go digging to find the answer.

This is the lesson your premedical training can teach. Without it, you will not make the grade in medicine.

FOUR

Premedicine:
Elective Courses and
Extracurricular Activities

IT IS EASY to see that the fulfillment of required courses will swallow up a great amount of your time during your first two years of premedicine. During your freshman year, for instance, you will be scheduled for three hours of lecture a week in English or English literature, three hours a week of foreign language, three or four hours a week of freshman chemistry lecture and recitation, plus four or five hours a week of chemistry laboratory. You may also be taking either math or physics during your first year.

And this is just classwork; you will have preparation work to swallow up your free periods and evening hours.

Nevertheless, the required courses still compose only three-fifths of your total college work, if that much. Furthermore, at least some of these required courses "overlap" courses you will be taking later in medical school to some degree. It is these facts which have led certain universities to experiment with combined premedicine and medical school curricula in an effort to shorten the total period of study. Johns Hopkins University, for instance, has been trying out such a program which amounts to five years of combined premedicine and medicine and two years of clinical (i.e., hospital) medical training . . . a total of seven years instead of eight.

In most colleges, however, you will have ample time (especially in your junior and senior years) for a wide range of nonrequired, or "elective," courses to fill out your work toward a bachelor's degree. You will also have some leisure time for other college activities which are not related in any way to your scholastic work, yet which play a very important part in your premedical work.

And here arises one of the big questions you will have to answer in premedical school: how can you best use your "elective" time? What elective courses should you take? Your answer will make quite a difference in determining what kind of doctor you become.

Giving Yourself Room to Grow In

Everybody knows what a bore is—but have you ever stopped to wonder what it is that makes a bore a bore?

If there is one person in the world from whom I will run and hide, it is a certain cousin of mine. Cousin John is the world's most colossal bore. It happens that he is an engineer, and a rather good engineer, too, judging by the firm he is working for and the kind of work he does for them, but as far as I am concerned, he is a terrible bore.

When you are talking to Cousin John everything is fine as long as you stick to engineering. In speaking of engineering he is witty, interesting, entertaining, even profound. But let the conversation veer just a trifle from his specialty field, and Cousin John just fades into the wall.

He has nothing to say. He has no interest in what anyone else is saying. He fidgets, and looks at his watch, and wonders if it isn't time to go home. Cousin John may be dynamite in an engineering crisis, but he is deadly anywhere else.

It isn't that this man is stupid, or dull, or even particularly ill-informed. He just isn't interested. He lives in the little world of his own special interest—engineering—and ignores everything else. The really tragic thing is that he will never be as good an engineer as he might be. He will never be able to talk to anyone except other engineers. He will never get any new ideas—except from other engineers. He has done all his growing in one narrow, specialized field, and it will handicap him for the rest of his life.

Exactly the same thing has happened to thousands and thousands of doctors.

Not so many years ago students preparing for medical school studied science, science, and more science. They studied practically nothing else. They took courses in biology, invertebrate zoology, vertebrate zoology, cat anatomy, embryology, bacteriology, histology, physiology, and any other kind of biological "ology" they could get their hands on.

If you asked them what sociology or history were, they would give you a blank stare. When you suggested that a course in creative writing or music appreciation might be broadening, they thought you were joking and laughed all the way to the biology lab.

But when they finished college and medical school they found themselves to be highly specialized, educated medical robots who were utterly unable to do or think anything except medicine. They had done all their growing in one narrow channel, just like Cousin John.

You might argue that they were better doctors because of it, but I doubt that they were. Quite a number of the finer medical schools in the country have begun to doubt it, too. In a recent Bulletin of the University of Pennyslvania School of Medicine the following statement appeared:

It is the opinion of the Admissions Committee and the Association of American Medical Colleges that the prospective medical student *does not increase his desirability by taking a large number of highly specialized science courses in college at the expense of a broader educational background.* After the requirements have been satisfied, the choice of other courses is left to the individual student. . . .

Medicine is an extremely broad subject, and knowledge of great diversity can be useful within its structure. Therefore, *students having a talent in almost any direction should be encouraged to pursue it in college.* Advanced knowledge of Chemistry, Physics, Mathematics or Engineering would be useful in certain types of medical work, and this is also true of such subjects as Psychology, Sociology, English Composition and Public Speaking. A good command of foreign languages is most advantageous. [Italics mine—A.E.N.]

Here we see one of the country's major medical schools giving carte blanche to the student to follow up whatever interest or talent he may feel inclined to follow, once the basic requirements we have described in the preceding chapter are satisfied or provided for. They did not cover the field in the above quotation; they might equally well have mentioned philosophy, history, or music.

The fact is that medical school itself provides a highly restricted and specialized course of study. There you will study medicine in theory and practice, and nothing else. You will have no time to think about anything but medicine, let alone read outside the field. During internship your single-minded concentration on things medical is even more intense; if you go on for residency training you will be concentrating not even on medicine as a whole, but on a single restricted segment of medicine.

Naturally you are eager to get to the heart of things, anxious to take courses that give you the feeling of being a medical student. You want the feel of the laboratory and the contact with biological sciences. But there are other things you will need in order to be a good doctor—things with no direct connection with medicine at all. Your college years are your last opportunity to explore other fields of study.

Exactly which fields you want to explore in your elective courses is strictly up to you. During your college years you will come in contact with a multitude of fascinating things that you never even knew existed. You may discover whole new fields of interest. It is possible, for instance, that somewhere during the four years you will begin to recognize history as something more significant than a parade of dates across a textbook page. One premedical colleague of mine became suddenly fascinated by our American Civil War and practically took a minor course in American history. Now he has completed medical school and is in residency training, but he has retained his interest in that aspect of our country's history. He is in fact a scholar of Civil War history, and is fast becoming an authority on one little-known aspect of it: Civil War medicine! It is only a hobby for him, but it has given him many hours of pleasure, and I believe he is a better doctor because of it.

At the very least, he is not a bore.

For you perhaps history is dull, but philosophy will strike a chord, contributing to your understanding of the world in general and medicine in particular. Possibly you will be attracted by the intricate channels and disciplines of formal logic. Or you may find new worlds of interest opening up for you in courses in psychology or sociology. Each person's preference will be different—but there is too much real fun in exploring these fields freely for you to cut yourself off from them without a look.

Will these intellectual explorations outside of scientific subjects hurt your chances for admission to medical school? On the contrary, your chances will be improved if anything. The board of admissions of the medical school will not interpret these explorations as disinterest in medicine on your part, but rather as evidence that you are seeking a broader base for your education than scientific courses alone could provide.

Finally, by exploring new pathways in college you may discover, perhaps to your surprise, that other fields of study are infinitely more exciting to you than medicine is.

Too many prospective medical students simply close their minds to the possibility that anything else might interest them. As a result, there are many men in medicine who are miserably unhappy as physicians. They walked through premedicine with their eyes closed and failed to recognize other interests they might have discovered.

Medicine is too stern a discipline to risk spending your life in it if you really don't like it. If there is something else you might want more, premedicine is the time to discover it.

College Can Be Fun

There is another part of college life, however, besides the prescribed and unprescribed course work you will be taking.

Many premedical students settle down to their studies with such grim determination that they forget that college can be fun, too.

Your premedical course work will not be so demanding that you won't have time to do anything else. Of course, there are always a few students in every class who hit the books every night of the week and crawl into bed too exhausted to do anything but catch a few hours of sleep before morning classes begin. These characters often walk off with straight A averages and give everyone around them an inferiority complex—but they are also the ones who finish college with the vague feeling that somewhere along the line they've been missing something.

You can do it that way if you want to, but you don't have to. There will be time for other things besides study, and those other things will make college life rich and exciting for you.

Every college and university has a broad range of these so-called extracurricular activities. In some cases they are quite specialized and related closely to your classwork: Chemistry Club or Physics Club, for instance, where interested students on their own time go into more advanced study and experimentation than the normal course load allows.

More often, extracurricular activities are completely divorced from the scholastic aspects of college work. Here we have the campus newspaper staff, the literary magazine or humor magazine, the radio and TV stations. You may wish to explore your dramatic inclinations with work in the college playhouse, or with the musical comedy group (these activities often offer opportunities for art work and writing, quite aside from acting and stage managing).

There are purely social activities, ranging from the all-inclusive life in college fraternities to such things as service on the junior prom committee, and Saturday night dates. Often there is intense political activity on campus which can be exciting as well as instructive.

Finally, there is the entire field of college sports.

These extracurricular activities exist for your fun and participation. The question is: how deeply should you get involved? Activities outside the classroom are an important part of college life; but obviously they are not all-important. It is quite possible to allow your interest in outside activities to run away with you to such an extent that your scholastic work suffers.

Where, then, can you safely draw the line? Do some activities involve more danger of this than others?

You will be perfectly safe if you bear one thing in mind: extracurricular activities are spare-time activities. This means the time left over when your classwork is under control.

If your classwork begins to sag in any given semester or if you realize that for some reason you just aren't hitting the mark in a given course or courses, that is the red flag which says slow down on outside activities. Not next semester, either; right now.

If you are happily involved in a number of activities, this can be extremely difficult to do. Nobody will make the decision for you; one of the nice things about college is that you are free to decide things for yourself. You have the freedom to do anything you want—including spoiling your scholastic record if you choose. The decision to cut down on outside activities when you need to will require a mature sense of values on your part, and maturity of judgment.

But that, too, is one of the things you are in college to learn. As you proceed with your medical education you must come more and more to rely upon yourself alone. Good common sense, and honesty, will show you the right direction if the decision must be made.

Taken in the right proportion, extracurricular activities can make the difference between a dull four years at the books and four years so full of interesting and exciting things that you don't know which way to turn. Take advantage of them!

What about College Sports?

Most extracurricular activities in college are so organized as to allow a student limited participation. He can do as much, or as little, in the activity as he feels he can safely handle. If he is working on the college TV station, for instance, he can cut down the amount of time he spends there if need be, or even quit for a while and resume activity later.

But college athletics are a somewhat different matter. During the season, and often during much of the rest of the year, major college athletics demand unlimited participation. Too often the sport assumes major importance and scholastic work minor importance.

This is particularly true in major sports such as football or basketball, where you must devote long, regular hours to practice when you might otherwise split that time between scholastic work and other extracurricular activities. You will be away from school for long weekends. You will be expected to fulfill your athletic obligations first, and get the schoolwork done when you can.

It can be done, of course. There have been outstanding college football and basketball players in premedical courses who have maintained their scholastic averages and gone on to become fine doctors. But in every case these were highly exceptional men.

Moreover, they took a grave risk of allowing their schoolwork to slide. A few can take that risk and have abilities exceptional enough to put it across. All too many discover too late that they are in too deep, and fail to make the grade into medical school.

If you try to carry a major sport and premedical studies at the same time, you are stacking the cards heavily against yourself. You may get away with it, but most likely you will not. It will be up to you to decide, in the long run, which is to take first place, medicine or athletics.

Understand that I'm not in any way condemning major college sports. I'm simply pointing out that there are only so many hours in a day, and only so much can be crammed into them. Unless you are an unusual student indeed, you can't handle a major sport and premedical studies and do credit to both.

For the athletically inclined premedical student the answer lies in the minor sports. Some of these have a limited season —baseball, for instance, or lacrosse, or crew. Others require limited practice which can be conveniently sandwiched into a crowded scholastic schedule—swimming is a good example. Two of my premedical classmates were on the wrestling team; it seemed to me that they were forever scientifically starving themselves down to their weight before a bout—but they could fit the sport into a heavy study schedule and keep up their grades as well.

Your own judgment is the best guide you can follow. If you recognize that a sport—or any other extracurricular activity— can monopolize your time if you let it, with obvious danger to your grades and class standing, you will be much less apt to allow it to happen. With judgment you can establish a balance, providing you recognize beforehand the dangers that can be present.

What about College Fraternities?

A great deal has been written for and against American college fraternities, and much of what has been said on either side has been pretty silly.

Whether they are all good, or all bad, or somewhere in between, it seems safe to say that college fraternities are here to stay, to some degree or another, for a long time to come.

On many college campuses fraternities play no part in college life because there aren't any. On other campuses the Greek-letter houses dominate every phase of college life. Wherever they are established they unquestionably represent a framework for college living, and thus exercise some degree of influence over the happiness of any student's college experience.

My purpose here is neither to applaud college fraternities nor to condemn them. I simply wish to raise the question of what part they should play in your thinking as a prospective medical student taking premedicine in college.

The advantages offered by college fraternities are well known. When a freshman student is pledged to a fraternity, he becomes a member of a group during a time when he might otherwise be quite lonely and confused making new friends and finding his spot in the hustle of college activity. He immediately becomes a part of a campus institution which has been there a long time and is recognized by others; therefore, the student feels recognized and accepted. He is met with fellowship and accepted by his fellow pledges and the fraternity brothers as "somebody" quite early in the game.

In the fraternity he will be living in a pleasant, homelike atmosphere. He will share the community property of the fraternity house. He will share in its social activities—its house parties, its block seating at football games, and so forth. In the house he will meet students of all classes in college and will have the use of the examination files and certain textbooks used by students in former years (although files of previous examinations are seldom as useful as they are touted to be).

There are, however, disadvantages to fraternity membership that often are overlooked by entering freshmen. When you pledge a fraternity you are in fact accepting your prospective fraternity brothers as your closest associates throughout your four years of college. You will be expected to render your first social allegiance to "the house," and to fit into the pattern of living at "the house." Undoubtedly you will make many close friends among your fraternity brothers, but you may at the same time miss the contact on campus with other students who might develop into rich friends. If you do make and maintain friendship with "outsiders" who do not meet with the full approval of your fraternity friends you may find yourself under a certain degree of pressure to drop the outside friends.

You may find that studying is difficult, and sometimes quite impossible, under fraternity house conditions. College fraternities are not, after all, study clubs. Although many houses pride themselves upon maintaining a high average of scholastic work, far too many others tend to sneer at too much studying. Nor does any given fraternity represent any study attitude on a national scale; the Phi Gams who excel scholastically on one campus may be low house on campus at another school, and rather proud of the fact.

This does not mean that fraternity membership is dangerous to the premedical student who must maintain his grades. It simply means that you will have to exert a bit more self-discipline (sometimes a lot more!) than if you were not associated with a fraternity. Fraternities can be fun to belong to. You just have to be careful that they don't become too much fun. There will be a surfeit of tempting distractions at all times if you allow yourself constantly to be tempted, and occasionally the distractions that are offered are hard to resist. On the other hand, in most houses a brother who is intent upon maintaining a good scholastic average will be respected and his fraternity friends will go out of their way to help him keep up his work.

Again, it is a matter of using a little mature judgment to

maintain a safe balance. A little is fine; a little more may be too much. You will have to decide for yourself where the balance line is.

If you like the idea of the "Greek" way of doing things on campus, fine—you'll enjoy membership and find that it carries rich rewards. If you don't particularly go for the idea in the first place, don't let yourself be forced. No college fraternity association will have much influence on a medical school board of admissions. Certainly nonmembership will never stand in your way. Nor will membership or nonmembership make much difference when the question of medical fraternities arises in medical school. Those groups are quite different from college social fraternities, as we will see in a subsequent chapter.

In summary, both scholastic work and extracurricular activities contribute to your preparations for the study of medicine. A happy balance between them will make your premedical training what it should be: a broad educational experience, with an opportunity to follow up fields of interest other than medicine; an opportunity to acquire working tools which will be both useful and necessary in medical school—tools of knowledge, tools of scientific experience, and most important of all, methods of study. These are the years of exploration and study. You cannot use them too broadly.

We have discussed the relationship of required courses, elective courses, and extracurricular activities in your preparation for medical school. Now we will consider a few of the special problems which will face you in college: problems of financing and of competition, for instance. Then we will go on to the big hurdle for which you have been preparing all through college—your application for admission to medical school.

FIVE

Premedicine:
Special Problems

QUITE ASIDE from the questions of courses and activities, you
will be facing a number of very practical problems during
your four years of premedical work.

Certain of these problems, such as grade averages, will
affect every premedical student. Others—such as the problem
of financing college—will concern some students more than
others. These are nevertheless potential problems for all pre-
meds. Before discussing the biggest practical problem of all—
medical school application—it might be wise to consider a
few of these other practical matters.

Grades Aren't (Quite) Everything

It's true—they aren't. They are important, however, and
can't be ignored unless you are one of these natural geniuses
who can't seem to get a poor grade no matter what you do.

College grades are different from high school grades. In
high school if you complete the required work in a course
with reasonable proficiency you may very probably receive an
A for your effort. In college the same program would almost
certainly bring you a B. Most colleges consider an A to be an
indication of really exceptional work, reserved for the unusual
student who has demonstrated an unusual grasp of the subject at hand and an unusual interest in it.

So the fact that you were valedictorian in high school does

not necessarily mean you will make a straight A record in college. Furthermore, you will be under much less pressure to do excellent work in college than you were in high school. College classes are often so big that the individual student is lost in numbers. Nobody but you will seem to care very much whether you do your work or not. Nobody will scold if you chuck your books in favor of an evening of beer at the corner tavern. In fact, many of your college friends will chuck their books in favor of the above-mentioned, especially if you can be persuaded to join them.

Trouble is, most of them won't be in premedicine.

How important are grades, then, in your overall chances of admittance to medical school? Much as certain progressive medical schools would like to de-emphasize the importance of grades, they still serve as the most reliable measure of how well a student has completed the scholastic part of his premedical training. Thus grades are very important when the board of admissions of a medical school begins reviewing applications for admission.

This is not to say that you need a straight A average to get into medical school. A good solid B average will meet the scholastic requirements of any medical school. Most if not all medical schools admit students with overall C averages if other factors appear to justify the action, according to a statement in the recent report on medical education in the United States of the *Journal of the American Medical Association*.

Generally speaking, the Board of Admissions would prefer to see A's earned in required courses and C's in electives rather than vice versa. A D in a given course doesn't necessarily scuttle your hopes for admission to medical school, but the Board of Admissions is going to wonder what it's doing there. A failure in a course will push eyebrows up even further.

Is it wise, then, for a student to repeat a course in order to "erase" a poor mark in an important course? Emphatically it is not. In the first place, it will not erase a mark at all; the poor mark will remain on the record regardless of what repeat grade is earned. Long experience has proved that the results of such a repetition are seldom better than the original grades. The student who has placed himself in the position where he feels he has to repeat a course had better ask himself why he got the poor mark in the first place, and face facts honestly. He does not belong in premedicine, and he's damaging the chances of other students who do.

Another practice that is prevalent among premedical students is to sign up for "gut" elective courses, courses with a reputation for being snaps where high grades can be obtained with little work. Courses like that can bolster a sagging grade average, true. But, again, let's face facts: It isn't honest. The student who does it is deliberately looking for a back door into medical school. He's asking for trouble, because there aren't any "gut" courses in medical school. . . .

So, you have a job to do to keep up your grades. You don't have to be a grind, but you do need a solid, better-than-average grade record to compete for a place in medical school.

If you are a quick student and a fast learner you may walk off with good grades with comparatively little effort. If you are a plodder you may earn them only after blood, sweat, and tears. Neither extreme is really either a benefit or a handicap. The fast learner is the one who is likely to slide, to let extracurricular activities get out of control, while the plodder may allow grades to preoccupy him unnecessarily at the expense of other things.

For the slow learner, good study habits may win half the battle. He may not actually be so slow at all; he may simply be wasting half his study time by inefficient habits.

As a premedical student you will be more aware of the importance of your grades than students in other fields, but you need not spend four years worrying about them. Learn to use your time and study efficiently; dig in harder if you see your grades sliding; do the best you can honestly do. The grades will come naturally.

The Competition Is Stiff

Competition in premedicine is one of the hardest things of all for many students to cope with. There are more students than there are seats in medical school—everyone in premedicine knows that. Naturally you are going to be competing with your classmates for those seats. Naturally you are going to feel the competition.

Now, this isn't particularly bad. A little competition is good for everybody. It keeps you on your toes. Competition will encourage you to open your books from time to time, and will make it easier for you to resist the alluring distractions that will keep coming your way.

So competition is fine, as long as you don't let it get you down. Unfortunately, it can do just that. Some students spend four years in college nursing a monster-size inferiority complex. They worry more about what their lab partner is doing than about how much they are learning. They labor fiercely for a grade of 81 per cent in an exam, and see the next fellow emerge with an effortless 94 per cent, and they wonder how they can ever hope to beat him out when it comes to medical school applications. Sometimes they worry so much they cut down their own efficiency severely.

There are always going to be people in your class who are smarter than you are. You can't do a thing about that fact but accept it. (There are also people who are dumber than you are, but they usually manage in some crafty way to conceal the fact.) Every premedical class has its eager beavers, too, who go about impressing everyone who will listen to them, including professors, with how extremely clever they are. These are the ones who ask the incomprehensible questions at the end of a lecture, and stand in the corridors before examinations talking about how many hours they have studied and how well prepared they are. They act as though they have been stabbed when they pull down a mere 92 per cent on a mid-term exam.

They can make you feel awfully stupid sometimes. At times like that it is good to remember that if you feel insecure about your work the eager beavers feel twice as insecure. They are just as much afraid of flopping as you are, really more so. They find it necessary to bolster themselves continually with a public show of wisdom and excellence. Of course, they often do good work, and get into medical schools—

But so do you.

So compete with them, but don't let them scare you. Tell yourself that their objectionable personalities will counterbal-

ance any good grades they may have. Think of all the energy
they are wasting. But, best of all, just ignore them and get on
with the business at hand, namely, doing an honest job to the
limit of your abilities without worrying too much about what
the other fellow is doing. The only way competition can hurt
you is by rattling you so much that you don't do the best job
you can do.

On Campus vs. Off Campus

For many students the question of where they will live
while going to college constitutes no problem at all. They will
be going to colleges remote from their homes, and naturally
will plan to live on campus.

Many other students, however, will have a choice to make,
especially those living in large cities or in heavily populated
states with good transportation systems. For these students,
college may be located within easy commuting distance.
Would it be better for them to live at home, or on campus?

Of course, you may not have a free choice. It is certainly
less expensive to live at home and commute to college if the
campus is reasonably close to your home. This is especially
true if your family is willing to provide room and board at
nominal cost, or no cost at all. For some, living at home may
be the only way you can afford to go to college at all, in
which case the decision is made for you.

But if you do have a free choice, the on-campus way is by
far the more desirable. At least during the junior and senior
years of college, I believe living on campus is almost as important as attending classes, and in many ways more important.

Nothing can be more deadening to the enjoyment of
friends and activities at college than a relentless struggle
against a railroad timetable or bus schedule. Frequently so
much time is spent in commuting that you feel you must get
home early in order to be ready for classes in the morning.
Too often the last train or bus for the night leaves just as
things are getting interesting.

But, most significant, the home-dweller misses out on the
greatest and most important intangible of college life: the

close hour-by-hour association with students and friends, whether in dormitories or in fraternity houses or even in rooming houses, during the period of intellectual exploration, which is the purpose of college. The bull sessions that start at ten in the evening and last most of the night are not foolishness; they are wonderful fun, and just as important in stimulating the student's ability to think as any classes are. The on-campus activities that go on until past midnight and end with coffee in the wee hours at Louie's are immensely important. The very sense of freedom to plan his time as he sees fit, from one dawn to the next, has its value as part of a student's education.

The benefits which accrue from living on campus are mostly intangible benefits. They can only be expressed by saying "it's more fun that way," but they actually amount to much more than just enjoyment. You may have trouble selling your folks on the idea, but college life involves more than study. You lose out significantly if you don't live on campus at least a part of the time.

A Fellow's Got to Eat, Too

Any detailed discussion of the cost of four years at college would be a waste of your time and mine. There is so much variation between schools that it is difficult even to talk in generalities.

You may be attending a college where tuition and fees alone will cost you a thousand dollars a year and your room and board another two thousand dollars, where club or fraternity activities are frequent and expensive, and where money, if it doesn't grow on trees, certainly disappears as if it did.

Or you may go to a college where you will pay, as a resident of the state, $25 a year in tuition, where room and board expenses are kept to a minimum by cooperative living arrangements, and where a dollar goes a long way.

Chances are that your school will fall somewhere between these extremes—but at any school there will be some charge made for tuition and fees each year, and your food and lodging will be an expense. Books will cost you a significant amount of money (though compared to what you will have to spend on them in medical school the expense is only a drop in the bucket) and their resale value, if you choose to resell them, will be negligible. In addition, you will need money for running expenses—clothing, laundry, dates, tobacco (if you smoke), etc.

So, money has to come from somewhere. If you are floating through on the strength of Dad's ample bank account, you can skip this section and go on to the next. You are lucky, and you have no worries, financially speaking. But the majority of college students aren't so lucky. Thanks to the high cost of living and the federal income tax Dad's bank account may not be so ample as it might once have been. In the past many student-veterans were substantially aided in paying their college expenses by the G.I. Bill; but the need for this, we hope, is also a thing of the past. Money available through the AMAERF program (which we will discuss later) is reserved for students already in medical school. So most college students these days have to foot part or all of the bill for premedical training themselves.

Where can the money come from?

Fortunately, we are living in a time when no intelligent student of promise needs to forego a college education solely because of lack of funds to put him through.

For one thing, there are many colleges and universities which are inexpensive to attend, and which provide quite as sound a preparation for medicine as the most expensive colleges in the country. If the state in which you live supports a state college or university, your tuition and fees as a resident of the state will be significantly lower than for out-of-state students. Every college publishes a bulletin of information regarding its courses of study and the costs to the student. Check the list of schools you might like to attend to see which will cost you less to attend in the first place.

Again, almost every college has certain funds set aside for scholarship or loan assistance for students who are in need of it. These funds seldom cover the whole expense, but they can help a very great deal.

Other scholarships are available to capable students. A number of industries, for instance, offer scholarships each year on a competitive basis. In some areas Pulitzer Prize scholarships are offered, to be won by competitive examination and interview. Your high-school adviser can provide you with information about these scholarships. Certainly they are worth trying for; if you win one, it can go a long way toward defraying your college expenses.

Finally, there are a multitude of ways that a student can earn part of his expenses even while he is in college.

If you are entering college on a shaky financial basis, your first step should be to consult with the dean or the registrar to discuss the problem with him. College authorities know that many students enter college with insufficient funds. They know what scholarship funds their particular college can offer to which students under what conditions. Often they must limit these funds to cases of frank and immediate need, but more often assistance in some amount, large or small, is available if you can convince the college authorities that you deserve it. Perfect frankness is your best friend in discussing such problems. Don't try to make yourself out a pauper if you aren't. On the other hand, don't be ashamed to admit your financial straits.

For part-time work, the student placement service of your college will be able to assist you. Many students wonder if it is safe to add a further burden of part-time work to an already crowded schedule. As long as the work is not too physically demanding and doesn't consume too much time, it can be undertaken safely enough. It may cut into your free time, but thousands of premedical students have carried part-time work and at the same time participated fully in all their college activities.

What kind of part-time work can you do in college? The kinds are legion. Anything that will pay you a few dollars for a few hours' work each week is worth considering. Naturally you will look for some way to use any work experience you have had previously. You may have more than one kind of job, and you may end up drawing funds from a multitude of sources. If they add up to enough, well and good.

Summer vacations offer you an opportunity to build up a fund for the following school year. Many jobs are available to college students for summer work; employers frequently like "summer replacements" to cover positions left open by regular employees on vacation.

Certain students come to college with funds in the bank saved over a period of years in small jobs. I carried newspapers and worked Saturdays in the local supermarket when I was in high school. The amount of money I had saved by the time I entered college seems ridiculously small now, but it was there when I needed it, and I needed it!

Subsequently, I carried quite a succession of part-time and summer jobs, including:

1. Summer work in the warehouse of a large chemical company, unloading freight cars.

2. Work as a night and weekend lab technician in the local hospital, covering emergency laboratory work. No previous experience here—the head technician taught me the work I needed to know.

3. Summer work in a steel factory to lay up a few hundred dollars for the following year.

4. Bus boy job in a local restaurant one year for my noon and evening meals.

5. A job in the college library working on the card files. Boring, yes, but I could fit it into a busy schedule, and got a dollar an hour for my time.

6. Summer work as a full-time replacement technician in the local hospital clinical laboratory.

7. Free-lance story writing, which began bringing in an occasional check in my senior year.

If this seems to be an awfully shaky and hodgepodge way to finance a college education, I certainly agree that it was. The important thing, however, is that it did the trick. It also demonstrates that a student can exploit a multitude of sources to obtain those precious and necessary dollars. Premedical students often work in hospitals as orderlies. Sometimes they find part-time work as technicians in clinical or commercial laboratories. Often there are jobs available in local or college cafeterias. Investigate every source you can think of; any kind of work is fair, as long as it does not interfere with your college work.

But if you find that it does—look for a different job. All the money in the world won't help you if you allow your important work—in college—to slide.

The Medical College Admission Test

This examination is probably the most universal requirement for admission to medical school—all accredited medical schools require it—and in many ways it is the most baffling requirement to the prospective medical student.

The Medical College Admission Test is a strange and wonderful examination. You will take it sometime late in your junior year of premedicine, if you intend to complete four years of college for a degree before medical school. The test is compiled by the Educational Testing Service in Princeton, New Jersey, and is given to students under security conditions that would make the Atomic Energy Commission jealous.

What is the test? It is comparable in some ways to the general examination required in many European colleges and universities. It is a daylong test, and no preparation for it is possible in the usual sense. It is concerned with your knowledge and ability in general; specifically, it seeks to assess, as closely as possible, your aptitude for your chosen profession—medicine.

Now, aptitude is a very difficult thing to measure. It doesn't necessarily have anything to do with knowledge of facts, or preparation, or anything else. Many of the questions on the test have little or nothing to do with premedicine or medicine. Nor is this the sort of test you pass or fail. Rather, your scores on the test are registered against a number of scales. Your overall position, with respect to your colleagues, on the scales is significant. Your overall results on the test indicate your (probable) aptitude as a prospective physician.

Certainly you will do best on this examination if you spend very little time worrying about it. When the time comes, go and take it. It is important to do the best you can in answering whatever questions the examination asks, but worrying about it and cramming for it will only make you the more confused when you begin it.

You will never know what result you obtained on the test,

nor will you ever know how your colleagues stacked up against you. The only positive thing that can be said is that when—and if—that precious acceptance to a medical school arrives in your mailbox, you will know that you can't have done too badly.

SIX

The Big Hurdle:
Application for Medical
School Admission

AS WE POINTED out in earlier chapters, there are a number of hurdles that a premedical student must leap in the course of his college preparation for medicine. Some of these hazards can be skirted or overcome without difficulty; some are much harder to surmount. You have seen classmates fall by the wayside during the first three years of premedicine. Some have failed to make the grade scholastically. Some have lost interest in medicine in favor of other fields more exciting to them. Others have been unable or unwilling to submit to the self-discipline necessary for completion of a successful premedical training.

But you have come through unscathed, and now at the beginning of your senior year of college you are facing the single most difficult hurdle in your quest for a medical degree: your application for admission to a medical school. This is the hurdle that can make or break your determination to become a doctor. But it is a different sort of hurdle from all the rest, for a very significant reason.

So far, everything you have done to work toward your goal has been very much under your own control. What you have done with your opportunities in college has been up to you . . . so much so, perhaps, that it has been a little frightening at times. You have been free to control your study time and extracurricular activities as you saw fit. You have had complete control over your scholastic record. When decisions had to be made, you made them yourself.

But the next hurdle—admission to medical school—is out of your control. All you can do is present your record to the Board of Admissions, appear at the appointed time for an interview, and hope.

It may be that you have a fine grade average to present; you may have been active in campus extracurricular affairs; you may have a compelling personality and a deep, sincere desire to become a doctor; you may have excellent recommendations from your professors. And yet you still may not be accepted for admission to a medical school. There may be no reason for this that is apparent to you or to anyone who knows you, but it still may happen. And that, to all intents and purposes, will be that as far as your study of medicine is concerned.

To make matters even worse, you may have classmates who you know have done poorer work and present poorer qualifications but who nevertheless are accepted to their first choice of medical school without difficulty.

If it seems unfair that this should be so—perhaps it is. Medical schools know and admit, to their very real regret, that inequities occur every year in filling out their class rosters. They know that they will inadvertently reject excellent prospective doctors and admit duds every year. They are constantly seeking ways to change this, but the inequities continue to occur.

At the bottom of the trouble is one big fact that cannot be avoided: there are not enough seats in medical school to accommodate the number of students who are qualified to occupy them. In 1962 there were eighty-two four-year medical schools in the United States and three schools offering two years of medical school, the basic-science years. In Canada there were eleven four-year schools and one basic-science school. Each year approximately fifteen thousand students are applying for seventy-five hundred seats in those medical schools. Although these figures are more favorable than a few years ago, they still can mean only one thing: somebody has to lose out. On the average, for every student who is admitted there is at least one other who is not.

You may be one of those who lose out.

Considering that every premedical student knows this, it isn't surprising that application time is a period of nervous tension and worry. You would have to be superhuman not to be worried. The medical schools don't believe in quick decisions, either; you may have to wait several months after your applications are complete before you receive the long white envelopes with the fatal news.

So you are going to worry about your medical school applications, come what may. But while you are worrying, perhaps one little fact (and it is a fact, believe it or not) will make you feel better:

The medical schools are just as worried as you are. If you want desperately to be admitted to medical school, rest assured that each medical school wants just as desperately to fill its first-year seats with the men and women, of all who apply, who will make the best doctors and do the best job of upholding the reputation of the profession and of that school as a place where fine physicians are trained.

Knowing that some applicants are going to be disappointed, you want to present your application in the best possible light. The decision will be based upon many factors. Is there anything that you can do, in applying, to further your chances of acceptance?

Of course there is. Making application for admission to a medical school is not simply a matter of filling out an application form and mailing it in. In this chapter we will discuss the problems of medical school applications, and see in what ways you can present your application most favorably. Many questions will arise for you to answer: Which medical schools should you apply to? How many? What will you need to complete your applications? How do you go about filling out the forms? What about personal interviews? How much does it cost to apply? It may be helpful to have some of these answers before the questions arise.

There are only two things uniformly true about applications to medical schools regardless of which schools you are applying to:

They are all due at the same time of year.

They will all cost you money to file.

In fact, aside from the time when applications are accepted (between September and December of the year previous to the year in which you want to enter) and the fee required to be submitted with the application (from $5 to $10, and in some cases more), every medical school has its own ideas of the questions it wants answered on the application form and how it wants them answered, as well as what other information should accompany the application to complete it for consideration by the Board of Admissions.

Nevertheless, each different application form is accompanied by specific instructions for completing it. You must read the instructions, keep the applications straight, and follow each set of instructions to the letter. There is no sense spending time and money submitting an application which will be thrown out in the first screening because something has been omitted. Medical schools quite rightly assume that a qualified applicant should be able to read and follow instructions to the letter.

Which Medical School Should You Apply To?

I have known prospective medical students who have sent applications to every medical school in the country that they thought might conceivably accept them. It took them a great deal of time and effort. It wore out their professors with letter writing, and it cost the students a tidy sum of money to do it. And actually it didn't do them a bit of good.

Choosing the medical schools you will apply to, and deciding how many, is a matter of time, money, and common sense.

Every application will cost a minimum of $5 out of hand, which is not returnable. It is not even credited against your tuition in the school that accepts you. Thus, if you apply to ten different schools your applications alone will cost you $50, and probably more. This sum is in addition to the cost of grade transcripts from your college, at perhaps $1 per application.

Furthermore, certain medical schools ask on their application form how many schools you are applying to; in some cases they want to know which ones. They expect a student to make a reasonable number of applications, but they may think it odd if a student is sending out twenty or more.

A sensible approach is to decide (1) which schools you would most like to go to and (2) which schools seem most likely to view your application with favor. Perhaps three schools for one reason or another seem like good prospects to you, with a fourth that is less attractive but still acceptable if the chips are down. Four schools is a good average number; this allows you a variety, doesn't cost too much, doesn't over-burden the people you will be asking for help, and probably offers you as good a chance as more, if you select the schools carefully.

But what factors should you consider in selecting the schools?

Among other things, your personal preference, your geographical location, the funds you have available, and each school's reputation as a medical school should be considered.

There are a few medical schools in the country which are generally considered to be "tops" by the profession. Such schools as Harvard Medical School, Cornell Medical School, University of Pennsylvania School of Medicine, Johns Hopkins, and Jefferson Medical College have long enjoyed a world-wide reputation as fine medical schools.

Most of these "top" schools have little or no restriction against students who apply from outside the state in which they are situated. Part of their reputation has arisen because they accept students from all parts of the country, and their graduates can be found practicing medicine in all fifty states.

But because of their reputation these schools often have a staggering number of applicants for the limited number of seats they have available. The University of Pennyslvania School of Medicine, for instance, frequently has as many as 2,-500 applications for its 135 first-year seats. Thus, for each student admitted 18 are rejected. Obviously any given student's chances in such a competition are poorer than at a school which receives only 200 applications for its 135 seats.

Many of the medical schools are state supported as part of state universities. These schools heavily favor applicants who are residents of the state; in fact, many such schools state flatly that they will not consider out-of-state applicants. If you are a resident of a state with such a school, one of your applications should almost certainly go there, for your chances will be much better there than elsewhere. It doesn't matter where you took your premedical training as long as you are legitimately a resident of the state in question.

You may protest that you've heard that the school in your state isn't very good. For some reason the residents of a state occasionally take a very provincial attitude toward their home-state medical schools. If you're really worried about the school's reputation, consult with your premedical adviser. The school's reputation may be very high—away from home. Find out where graduates of the school have obtained internships. Talk to physicians from other parts of the country regarding the school.

But, generally speaking, if a medical school is accredited by the Association of American Medical Colleges, you can be confident that it will provide you with a good medical education. In the profession you will be judged much less by the school you attended than by how you conduct yourself as a physician.

If you are a resident of a state which has no medical school as part of its state university you will be forced to face the competition elsewhere. Choose schools which make little or no geographic distinctions. Check their enrollment statistics over past years to make sure that they do indeed accept out-of-state students in significant numbers. Don't waste your applications where they will do you no good. This sort of information is to be found in the annual Bulletin of the Association of American Medical Colleges, entitled "Admission Requirements of American Medical Colleges." Your college library will have a copy on its shelves; you will find much interesting and valuable material there relating to admission practices of American medical schools.

One word of warning: Certain medical schools in this country are not accredited by the Association of American Medical Colleges. A school must earn its accreditation, even a fine new medical school being established as part of a state university. No new medical school will be accredited until it has carried its first class through all four years. Well-established institutions starting medical schools can be relatively certain of their accreditation as soon as this requirement is fulfilled, but there are, and have been in the past, some schools from which accreditation has been withdrawn, or was never granted.

Students graduating from nonaccredited medical schools have serious stumbling blocks in their path throughout their professional lives. You take a risk in entering any such school, and would be wise to avoid them. Once again, reference to the Bulletin of the Association of American Medical Colleges will tell you if the school you are considering is properly accredited.

What about Two-Year Medical Schools?

These are the schools which do not have the clinical facilities—that is, hospitals, medical faculty, etc.—to teach the last two years of medicine, but are well equipped to teach the first two years, the so-called basic medical sciences. In 1962 there were three such schools in the United States: Dartmouth, North Dakota and South Dakota. These schools are fully accredited for the first two years of medicine, and have enviable records of advanced-standing admission of their graduates in four-year medical schools for the final two years of their training. In fact, in 1962 every single one of the 107 graduates of these schools found a place in the junior class of a four-year school. In addition to these three schools, Brown University, Rutgers University and the University of New Mexico are planning construction of two-year basic science schools in the near future and Idaho State and Brandeis University are considering similar plans.

These are all fine schools, as far as they go. However, if you start your medical studies in any two-year school, you will have to seek admission at advanced standing to a four-year school later. Fortunately most four-year schools have openings in their classes at the beginning of the third year, and can absorb students from these basic-science schools.

How Do You Go about Applying?

Once you have decided upon the medical schools to which you wish to apply—you should have made this decision by the beginning of your senior year of premedicine—you must write to each of them requesting application forms. A fancy letter is not necessary; this is not the time or place to attempt to impress anyone. However, any correspondence with a medical school should be typewritten if at all possible, and as neat and clean in appearance as you can possibly make it.

A letter such as the following will do very nicely:

> 78 Easton Avenue
> New Brunswick, N. J.
> September 5, 19—

Director of Admissions
University of Pennsylvania School of Medicine
36th and Chestnut Streets
Philadelphia, Pennsylvania

Dear Sir:

At the present time I am a senior premedical student at Rutgers University, and expect to receive my bachelor's degree in biological sciences next June.

I would like to apply for admission to the University of Pennsylvania School of Medicine for the year beginning September, 19—. Would you please send me the necessary application forms, and a copy of the current Bulletin of the Medical School?

> Yours very truly,

That's all you need to say. You are telling them that you are at least qualified to apply, and that you want application forms and the current bulletin of information (if you do not already have access to it). Anything else is superfluous at this time. Notice that this letter should be sent to "Director of Admissions," regardless of the medical school.

I am assuming that you are completing four years of premedicine and expect to take a degree. If you are applying for admission to medical school after three years of college, you will follow exactly the same procedure except that you will start your applications off during your junior year rather than your senior year.

You can send this letter to the medical schools during the summer months, of course, but if you organize your "application work" during September and October, September is early enough to write your first letters. Just don't put it off much longer. You may need a few extra weeks before deadline in which to work.

It will take the medical schools anywhere from one to three weeks to send you their application forms. In the meantime there are certain things you can arrange to speed your applications through when they arrive.

1. Have a picture taken. Every application will require a photograph of you, usually 2½ by 3½ inches. The photo should be quite recent, and should be a studio-type portrait rather than a snapshot. Senior yearbook pictures usually are not ready in time. If you haven't had a picture taken in the previous six months, better have a new one made by a studio or a good amateur friend. Obtain the negative, so that you can order larger or smaller prints quickly if need be.

2. Check on the machinery for obtaining transcripts from your college. These transcripts of your grades will not be given to you personally—they will be sent directly to the medical schools when the time comes—but you can save time by finding out now where to request transcripts at your college, from whom, how long they will take when you are ready for them, and what you will be charged for them. Most colleges provide a copy or two free, and then charge perhaps $1 a copy thereafter. If you find these things out in advance, you will be ready to move quickly when the application forms arrive.

3. Start thinking about your references. Your application forms may require a variety of references, but most require two kinds: references from professors in scientific courses and character references.

For the first type of reference, select a professor or instructor who knows you the best, not necessarily the one from whom you have received the best grades. Medical schools receive very few bad reference letters. They will be much more interested in a letter saying, "I know Joseph Brown personally as a student, and have observed his work in my classes and feel he will be an excellent physician," than in one saying, "This man must have done acceptable work in my class because I seem to have given him an A in analytical chemistry."

If you are attending a large university you may discover that you do not know any of your professors personally. In this case consider the men in the various departments with whom you have had the most contact, and ask them if they will be willing to provide reference letters. In some schools "departmental letters" are signed by the heads of the biology and chemistry departments after conference with all the faculty members in the department. In such cases you can still consider which men have known you the best and alert them that you are making applications. Often they will add personal notes to the departmental letters.

In any event, start thinking about your choices before you have the applications in hand. For personal or character references, try to avoid relatives even if nothing is said about this on the application forms. Consider people who have known you for a period of years, and ask them frankly if they will be willing to write letters of recommendation for you, and if they honestly feel that they can recommend you highly.

4. In preparation for the application forms, buy a large manila folder for each application you intend to send, and mark the name of the school in large letters on the outside of each. Place in each the carbon copy of the letter you have written (keep carbons of all correspondence). When the application forms arrive, along with instructions, place each one in its proper folder. It is very easy to get the various requirements of different schools badly confused, especially if you are applying to four or five; the use of folders will keep them separate, with all the material connected with any given application in one place.

When your application forms arrive, read each of them through carefully, twice. Then take a separate sheet of paper for each application and note down the specific things it requires other than the answers to its questions, as well as any other pertinent data such as deadlines for filing, etc. Your "tally sheet" on one application may look like this:

Univ. of Penna.
1. Deadline for completion of application: Jan. 1.
2. Interview: says "Not required but preferable." May write for appointment if not notified. (Note: write by Nov. 1 if not called previously.)
3. Requires 2½ by 3½-inch photo.
4. Requires grade transcript.
5. Requires results from Medical College Admission Test (write Educational Testing Service to send).
6. Three scholastic references (Prof. A, Prof. B, and Dr. C).
7. Two personal references (specifies medical or clergy) (Dr. X, Rev. Y, possibly Dr. Z).
8. 100-word essay on why I want to be a doctor (space provided on application form—specifies longhand).

By using this sheet as a checklist you can see at any time what you have obtained and what is still due for that particular school. You also keep the deadline always before you so you will not risk coming in too late.

The next step is to fill out the application sheets, answering the questions as briefly and accurately as possible. Don't try to second-guess the purpose of the questions in your answers; just be honest and be sure you give complete answers.

Since this application is to be read by a number of people who want the information on it, fill it out so that they can read it. Typewrite if at all possible (except those sections where longhand is specified). Keep erasures and corrections to a minimum, and spell correctly. Nothing gives a worse impression than an application form with a flock of misspelled words!

If I seem to be harping unduly on the crass mechanical aspects of this matter, it is with good reason. A board of admissions must read hundreds of such applications. The easier they are to read the better. You might easily impress them with your neatness; you will certainly impress them with your sloppiness. Make it as neat a job as you can.

Once the forms are filled in, notify your references. Most

application forms will merely ask for their names and addresses; give them, and let your references know that they will soon be hearing from such-and-such a medical school.

Order your transcripts sent. If you have not already done so, notify the Educational Testing Service to send your Admission Test results to the school.

When your checklist is complete and the application form is finished, mail it back to the school. If you wish, you may write a brief covering letter informing the director of admissions that your grade transcripts are coming, and so forth. Don't use the opportunity to plead your case for admission. Your applications and letters are part of your case. Your interview will be your chance on stage.

What about the Interview?

While there is no unimportant part of your application, probably no single part will be quite so important as your interview with a member of the board of admissions.

At best the board of admissions gets a "paper image" of you from your application form and reference letters. This may in fact give a false impression of what sort of person you really are. The medical schools recognize this, and consequently place a great deal of faith in the personal interview in making their selections.

You may be requested to appear for an interview at a specific time, if you live within easy reach of the medical school. If you live at a distance, the school may ask you to make an appointment for a time when you will be available. In such a case, write promptly and state a choice of days when you can appear for an interview. Even your initiative in asking may be considered a significant factor by the medical school.

Once the appointment is made, keep it, appearing on time. Give the best appearance you can. The interview may last only five minutes as you speak briefly to one of the members of the board of admissions, or it may last half an hour. You may be asked about your interests in medicine, or your interests outside of medicine. You may be asked about world events, or about your extracurricular college activities. Very probably you will be asked why you want to be a doctor. By this time you should know the answer to that question, and be able to express it readily and sincerely.

Above all, try not to worry more than absolutely necessary. Your interviewer will not be an ogre; he is not going to try to trap you or make you feel uncomfortable. He already knows that you will be nervous and ill at ease. Try to give as natural an appearance as possible, and trust your natural pleasing personality to come through. It will, if you give it a fighting chance.

The Long Wait

You will discover that the business of completing applications will take an amazing amount of time and effort. If you're lucky you will maintain passing grades while the process of applications is going on.

But with your applications all completely filed, you sit back and wait. There is no other topic among your colleagues now. The talk will be exclusively of applications and interviews and recommendations, and will they or won't they? As time passes the tension increases. You convince yourself a dozen times that they just can't turn you down, and then you remember the C you pulled down in organic chemistry last semester and wonder if that one thing may mean your downfall. You hear somebody telling everyone who will listen about his interview at such-and-such a school, and how the interviewer all but told him he was accepted right on the spot —but you notice that the lucky fellow somehow doesn't seem any less worried than anyone else.

Then one day one of your friends comes to class with that unmistakable smile on his face, and the word is around class like a brush fire: Jones is going to Hopkins! or Bramlett's in at the university! You will be honestly happy for Jones or Bramlett, and still be sick with worry because you haven't heard anything from anybody yet. . . .

These results come in slowly. You may receive a letter from one or two of your applications, regretting to inform you that you have not been accepted. But then, perhaps as a Christmas present, perhaps not until February or March, you receive the long white envelope in the mail with the notice saying, "We are happy to inform you that you have been accepted as a member of the class beginning September, 19—" and requesting a $50 deposit against your first year's tuition, payable within ten days.

And you know that the biggest hurdle of all is behind you. You are on your way to becoming a Doctor of Medicine.

But suppose, you say, that the acceptance comes from your third-choice school before you have heard from your first-choice school. What do you do then?

Once a medical school has decided that they want you, they want you. They will request a deposit, often $50, sometimes $100, which must be paid at the time you accept a position in their class, usually within two weeks of notification.

Perhaps you feel reasonably confident that your first-choice school, School A, is going to accept you, yet here is School C already offering you a position in its class. Perhaps you would much rather go to School A, but you hardly dare turn down School C unless you are certain School A will come through. The deposit School C requests is applicable on your first year's tuition, but is not returnable if you accept the seat and then later turn it down. What to do?

You can, of course, pay the deposit to School C, accepting their proffered seat, and then forfeit it if School A accepts you later. But a more sensible thing—and the thing which is fairer to everyone concerned—is to write School A a letter, air mail special delivery, telling them that you have already been accepted at another school, and asking them if they could render a final decision on your application to them without delay.

This is not blackmail, it is simply stating facts. It should not be an appeal, either. School A can well recognize that you prefer them simply from the fact that you are withholding immediate decision on the other school—so you need not tell them. Under such circumstances, School A will probably review your application at once and, if they want you, will let you know accordingly. Or they may simply scratch your name from their list of applicants and congratulate you on your acceptance at School C. In any event you lose nothing, you do not cheat School C (who, after all, accepted your application in good faith and acted upon it) and you may gain prompt attention from School A.

Once you have accepted a position in a class, common courtesy demands that you write the other schools considering your applications at once and ask that they be canceled. This will relieve them of some of the strain of numbers, and bring your colleagues their acceptances faster. There is no particular glory in turning down acceptances that arrive too late. Be sporting about it.

Some Lose Out

But suppose, when the dust has settled, you have nothing but regret letters in your file—what then?

It isn't the end of the world.

There is no back door to medicine. Either you are accepted in a medical school or you aren't. If you are thinking of any approaches other than straightforward application for admission, forget them. They won't do you any good.

But there are certain things you can do.

First, realistically appraise your own record. It is often very difficult to be honest with yourself about a thing that means so much to you, but try to look at the record objectively. Perhaps your work really is not of medical school caliber. If it isn't, try to face the fact and seek other fields of interest. You will save yourself a great deal of heartache if you do.

If you still feel that your work is sufficiently good to qualify you for medical school, you may choose to go on in college for a master's degree, and then make application to other medical schools the following year.

There are other alternatives. There are fine medical schools in England and Scotland, and some fine schools on the Continent. You can easily ascertain which of these are considered "acceptable" by the American Medical Association and make applications. I know at least one physician who failed to be accepted by an American medical school and subsequently studied medicine at the University of Glasgow. He has passed licensure examinations in the United States and now is successfully practicing medicine here.

This is not a preferred procedure, simply because American medical schools are generally the best in the world today. Foreign schools are often regarded as "second-rate" by the profession, whether rightly or wrongly. But if all else has failed, this is at least a possibility.

Another possibility lies in seeking professional training in one of the many fields closely allied with medicine. Dentistry is a fine profession and a scientific discipline in its own right, and very much resents the suggestion that its ranks are filled with disappointed would-be physicians. This is nevertheless true, to some degree. Many students who do enter dentistry as a "second choice" discover that it is quite as fascinating a study as medicine; before they finish they are wondering why they had not set their sights on dentistry in the first place.

Much the same can be said for veterinary medicine, and for the whole host of professions and semiprofessions that make up the so-called auxiliary medical services: nursing, physical and occupational therapy, X-ray technology, laboratory technology, medical editing, and medical illustration, to name a few.

Finally, there are fields of work in the sciences related to medicine but not associated directly with it: physiology, chemistry, biochemistry, physics, and many others. There are places in both research and industry for men and women trained in these fields; you may find your place in graduate work here.

There is a common complaint that the aspiring physician must put all his eggs into one basket, that is, premedical training, and if he fails to be admitted to medical school he is not prepared by his college training to take a job in any other field. This may be valid if you look upon your college education as an education for a trade rather than as a broad educational basis for adult living. One medical educator, Dr. William Kennedy of the University of Pennsylvania, has answered the argument by pointing out that if the student had been admitted to medical school he would have spent five years or more learning to make his living in medicine. In the event that he is not admitted, Dr. Kennedy maintained, it would not be unreasonable to expect him to spend some time after graduation from college in learning to make a living in some other way.

But we will assume that you are among the fortunate. You have your acceptance to a medical school—and presumably are not so shaken by receiving it that you flunk all your senior courses! (It has happened, and it's very embarrassing for all concerned.) Now you can settle back and direct your attention to the mopping-up operations at college, terminating in your graduation in June with a bachelor's degree. June will seem a long way off, and the summer following even longer in your eagerness to get into the real business of studying medicine. The fact that you are already well along in your doctor's training won't seem nearly so important as the fact that the most exciting years are ahead.

But September will finally arrive and you will be stepping out into a completely different world from any you have known before. Here is the goal you have been working toward for the past four years: medical school.

SEVEN

Medical School:
The Broad View

IT IS UNLIKELY that you will ever again have to make such a tremendous jump as the jump from college to medical school.

Your first few weeks in medical school will be the most difficult you have ever experienced. You will be walking without any briefing into a different sort of world from any you have encountered before. You may not be able to tell at first just exactly how things seem to be different, but there will be no doubt in your mind that the difference is there.

Entering medical school is an exciting experience, and in many ways a frightening one. Certainly the jump from college to medical school is ten times the magnitude of the jump from high school to college.

Once more you will be at the bottom of the ladder. Somebody once remarked that the whole process of medical education is a matter of climbing to the top of ladders and falling off them again. It's true. You climbed to the top of the ladder in grade school, and fell off the top to become a high-school freshman. You climbed up again to become a senior in high school, and plop! back down to freshman again, this time in college, a longer and harder fall than before. But you picked yourself up and began climbing again. Finally you reached the exalted heights of a college senior, a leader in extracurricular life, doing all the things that only a college senior can do. . . .

And now here you are at the bottom again. This time it

seems that you fell a long way. This time the climb up again appears incredibly long and difficult. Even the second-year medical student you encounter on the street or in the cafeteria seems like a seasoned veteran, incredibly higher on the social and professional scale than you.

Of course, this up-and-down business is an old story to you by this time. But now something new has been added. The thing that is so new and different about medical school is the attitude of everyone around you: upper-class students, professors, instructors, even your own freshman colleagues.

College was never like this.

In college you were involved in many different interests and activities. Some of your courses were scientific, of course, but you studied many other things too. You were involved in extracurricular activities and perhaps, to some degree, in college sports. You had time which was very much your own to divide between your studies, your social activities, and your extracurricular activities. You had some time to spend just sitting looking at your feet if you chose.

In short, your attention was drawn in many directions. You had many interests and many purposes.

But in medical school you soon become aware of a great singleness of purpose. If your college studies were spread out to cover the broadest possible range, just the opposite is true in medical school. Here your work will be highly specialized, channeled down into a narrow groove and held there.

Everything in medical school is concentrated on the single task at hand: learning medicine. Everywhere there is the feeling of having too much to learn and too little time to learn it in. There is no time for distractions. There is only one job to do, no other.

Furthermore, in medical school you have no choice of what you will study. There are no electives. Everything is prescribed for you from the first day of the first year until the last day of the fourth. There is a great deal of material which everyone must cover, and nothing is so unimportant that you can choose it or ignore it according to your inclinations.

You will discover, perhaps to your horror, that a very great deal is expected of you in your studies—far more so than was the case in college. In fact, the college attitude toward studies

will seem almost lackadaisical in comparison to the demands
upon your time in medical school. You will have to toe the
line from the first day, keeping up with the work at all costs,
because so much is passing before you each day that to fall
behind would be fatal.

You will spend your day (all day—no free periods, no cut
classes) in laboratories and lecture rooms, from eight in the
morning until five at night with an hour for lunch in the
middle. After dinner in the evening you will retire to your
room to study from seven until eleven or later—not occasionally, but every night without fail, six nights a week—and
you will use Sundays as a chance to catch up with the things
you have let slide during the week.

And still you will not have time enough for the studying
you have to do.

There will be other things besides lectures, laboratories,
and textbooks, of course. You will make new friends. There
will be medical fraternities and social activities (of which
more later). You'll steal an occasional night out for a movie,
or an occasional hour to watch TV. But in medical school
these things are not second or third in importance—they are
so far down the list that they hardly rate mentioning. They
just don't count. Nothing counts—except learning medicine.

The Trees and the Forest

Much of your time in the first two years of medical school
will be spent learning facts—thousands and thousands of apparently disconnected, isolated facts. You will face the same
problem faced by generations of medical students before you:
the problem of learning pages and pages of facts that don't
seem to relate to anything.

Learning facts solely for the sake of learning them is probably the hardest thing in the world for anyone to do, yet that
is exactly what you will be asked and expected to do, and
you'll do it, too. The facts that you will be learning are
certainly related, in a broad view. They are like pieces in a
puzzle—quite incomprehensible in themselves because you
don't yet know what the picture is. And unfortunately there is
no time, in the first year of medicine, to show you how all

these facts relate to the study of medicine. You almost have to take it on faith that the things you are learning are important and will eventually fit neatly into place to form a complete picture.

Not long ago I was preparing to take an examination for medical licensure in the state of Washington. The examination had a section on the basic medical sciences: anatomy, biochemistry, physiology, and so on. Naturally, I had spent considerable time preparing for the exam, but one of my colleagues who was also taking it put my feelings into words perfectly when he said, "If only I could go through medical school again now. There was so much I missed, and so much I didn't understand at all!"

I belive that there is nothing more abundantly true about medical school training: for everything you learn there will be ten times as much that you don't learn, and still more that you don't understand.

How can this be? How can you hope to become a good doctor if you are going to miss so much that is offered in medical school, and fail to understand so much more?

The fact is that the average medical student is so deeply buried among the trees that he never gets a look at the forest at all. He becomes so deeply involved in learning the details of anatomy, or of physiology, or of pathology, that he fails to see the broader significance of what he is learning until much later. He has great difficulty connecting the details he is learning with the broader questions of human illness and human health. He is constantly asking himself, "What does this fact mean? How will I be able to use this bit of information? Is this really important or not? How does it apply to patients and diagnosis and treatment?"

You, as a medical student, will constantly be asking yourself the most important question of all: What do I have to know in order to be a doctor?

Part of the purpose of this book is to give you an occasional glimpse of the forest as well as the trees. As we discuss the things you will study in medical school I hope you will see the broad view as well as the details. You will be immersed in details constantly all through medical school; perhaps here, at least briefly, we can see the whole picture.

The Pattern of Medical School

In the next few chapters we will follow your course through a typical medical school in some detail. What *do* you study in medical school? How do you study it? How do you go about learning to be a doctor? Every medical school is somewhat different from any other, but the great majority of them follow the same general pattern in teaching their medical students. Briefly, the organization is like this:

THE PRECLININCAL YEARS. The first and second years of medical school are sometimes called the "basic-science years" or "preclinical years." During this time you will have very little to do with patients or hospitals, diagnosis or treatment. Your time will be spent learning about the living human body—its structure and how it works—in a great deal of detail. First you will study normal structure and function; then you will consider structure and function of the body in disease.

You will learn what diseases are, and how they alter the normal structure and function of the body. You will learn about drugs, and how they can modify the changes that occur in disease.

Your work will be both in laboratory and in lecture hall, but mostly in laboratory. Among other things you will discover how much is not known about the human body and its functions, and how the search for new knowledge progresses.

THE CLINICAL YEARS. During the third and fourth years your attention shifts from theory to practice. Much of your time is now spent in clinic and hospital ward, caring for patients. Under careful supervision you will in effect become "doctor" to the patients you see, learning from them as well as from your instructors. You will spend much time learning diagnosis—what is wrong with the patient—and treatment— what to do about it. You will become skillful in the highly specialized form of detective work a physician must use every day in caring for his patients.

Finally you will enter your "fifth year of medical school," the internship year. Here you will put into practice all that you have learned in the previous years, and you will continue to learn from experience with patients and from responsibility in caring for them.

Each part of medical school has its special problems as well as its special studies. But each part is, in fact, only a part of the broader picture: learning what you must know in order to be a doctor.

EIGHT

Medical School:
The First Year

IT MAY SEEM disappointing at first that you will not plunge immediately into the melee of patients and hospital beds, illness and diagnosis and therapy, when you start in medical school. You hear the words "preclinical" and "clinical" bandied about, and it seems to you that "preclinical" somehow smacks a bit of "premedicine." Perhaps it seems that instead of something new and excitingly different you are merely going back to the salt mines again—deeper salt mines, with longer working hours, too—for another two years.

But it makes good sense, if you try to see the broad view.

An auto mechanic would not get far diagnosing and treating the ills of your car if he didn't first have a pretty thorough working knowledge of how that car is put together and of what makes the various parts of it go when you press the starter.

By the same token a physician would have a hard time indeed learning to diagnose and treat human illness if he didn't understand quite well how the human body was made, and what made it run when the various parts were assembled. The doctor must know the normal, well-functioning human body inside and out before he can do very much to help with an abnormal, malfunctioning human body.

This is your job in the first year of medical school.

The study of the structure of the human body is known as *anatomy*, and is usually divided into two parts: the *macro-*

scopic, or gross, study of the organs and organ systems which make up the body; and the *microscopic*, or *histological*, study of the tissues and cells that make up the organs and organ systems.

But equally important is the function of those tissues and organs in the living human being. This study of how the body works is known as *physiology*. It will occupy part of your time in the first year. At the same time you will learn that the basis of all the physiological functions of the living body in the final analysis lies in certain groups of chemical reactions. The study of this "chemistry of life" is aptly called *biochemistry*.

These three studies of normal structure and function—anatomy, physiology, and biochemistry—comprise your first year's work. By studying the normal structure and function of the human body you will be laying a solid groundwork for your understanding of what sorts of things can go wrong and what can be done about them.

Anatomy: The Groundwork of Medicine

No matter which medical school you attend, you will be studying anatomy from the first day that classes convene.

For a period of several months you will be learning human anatomy. In schools where the "big three" are taught in a block system, you will be learning nothing but human anatomy for the first half year. You will be thinking anatomy and sleeping anatomy. You will be discussing anatomy at breakfast, lunch, and dinner, and studying anatomy until the early hours every morning.

There is a very great deal of anatomy to be learned.

You will discover that there is surprisingly little lecture. The medical schools have long since learned that the student does not learn anatomy in lecture halls, nor by studying lecture notes. He learns it in the dissecting laboratory, dissecting a human cadaver. Whether you like the idea or not, that cadaver will be your closest associate for your first months of medical school, and you will never forget him.

You will have a place at a table in the dissecting laboratory —a long, low room equipped with row upon row of tables,

seats, and study racks for books. You will probably share your
cadaver with two or three other students who will be your
dissecting partners. You will work together in the dissection,
and help each other study as you progress from portion to
portion of the cadaver.

You will probably have three textbooks to use in anatomy.
Every medical student has a copy of a major anatomy text—
Gray's or Morris' *Human Anatomy*. In addition you will have
a dissecting "atlas" and probably a "regional method" textbook of anatomy.

The reason for so many books becomes clear at the dissecting table. The best way to organize a complete anatomy
textbook is according to organ systems. Thus in your Morris'
or Gray's you will find long sections dealing with the arteries
and veins; another section dealing with the heart; another
concerned with the bones; another with the digestive system,
and so on.

But in the dissecting room you must necessarily dissect by
regions. If you are dissecting the neck, for instance, you will
find skin, layers of fascia, muscles, blood vessels, nerves, and
bones all present. These will begin below the region you are
dissecting and end above the region. So you must learn the
dissection region by region as you come to them, and at the
same time study the organ systems bit by bit.

Often such a method of study will seem very helter-skelter
and piecemeal at the time. Only when you have finished
completely can you see the relationships of the systems
clearly as they pass through the regions.

We have spoken earlier of medical jargon; in anatomy you
will begin to learn it well. You will describe things as being
"proximal" and "distal" rather than "close" and "far away."
You will speak of the "inferior aspect" of a structure rather
than the "bottom side" of it. You will learn long Latin names
for bones and muscles, blood vessels and nerves.

It will become very confusing. But, as we said before, there
is a sound purpose behind the jargon. As you learn to use it
you will discover that it enables you to describe what you
want to describe, accurately, in a few words rather than in
paragraphs. It ensures that another doctor will know exactly,

not just vaguely, what you are talking about. This can be of the greatest importance in practicing medicine.

Of course, it will also permit you to sound like a doctor very early in the game when you are home for Christmas!

As you progress through gross anatomy you will completely dissect your cadaver. You will learn the use of dissecting instruments. You will gain an understanding of the true size, shape, and appearance of the body's organs—something no textbook can convey. You will begin to appreciate the relative strength and delicacy of the tissues making up the human body.

Possibly you will have a graduate physician—usually a resident in surgery—dissecting a cadaver in the laboratory, keeping a little ahead of your progress, so that you can refer from time to time to his "prosection." You will have a skeleton to study, X rays to examine, and a "bone box." Finally, you will have your textbooks with their endlessly detailed descriptions and their pictures which somehow always seem more complex than the text.

With the help of all these things, you will learn anatomy.

Microanatomy: The Tissues and the Cells

The microscopic structure of the tissues of the human body is quite as important as the gross structure, and you will probably study the two aspects of anatomy side by side.

Microscopic anatomy—or *histology*, as it is sometimes called—is a much cleaner business than gross anatomy. Your hands don't get greasy, and the lab doesn't smell so badly of formalin. Only your eyes take punishment, for you learn microanatomy with a microscope and a slide box and a textbook and many hours spent peering at rows of cells trying to identify what the textbook says is there.

You learn very early in the game that nothing in the textbook looks even remotely like what you see under the microscope. Just as in gross anatomy, you will not learn primarily from lectures or from reading. You will learn by examining slides prepared from the various tissues of the body.

When I was a first-year student my microanatomy professor chose to give his lectures immediately after lunch each day, from one to two in the afternoon. I am certain that not more than 10 per cent of the class ever stayed awake through an entire lecture, especially when the professor turned off the lights and projected slides on the wall. I think the professor had decided that if we were going to take a snooze after lunch, we should snooze through a lecture and not over our microscopes.

Because it was over our microscopes that we learned microanatomy.

For all the long hours and hard work, there were things which brightened our days. There were several girls in our class, long-suffering creatures who were constantly tormented by the preponderance of males. A favorite trick was to wait until one of the ladies stepped away from her microscope for a moment, and then rim the eyepieces with lamp black. All attempts at dignity were futile when the young lady arose from her 'scope an hour later, owl-eyed, with black circles around her eyes.

One of the girls resisted all attempts to ruffle her calm until one of the boys slipped a tiny caterpillar into her microscope eyepiece one day. The sight of a fuzzy black something crawling across her slide of squamous epithelium was too much for her; from that day on she took her eyepiece with her whenever she left her lab seat.

But for the most part microanatomy is serious business. Gradually you begin to correlate the microscopic appearance of tissues with the gross appearance in the dissecting laboratory, and your picture of the normal structure of the human body begins to take a reasonable shape.

Neuroanatomy: The First-Year Graveyard

If you were to ask a class of graduating doctors which single course they thought was the most difficult in all medical school, chances are good that 75 per cent of them would name neuroanatomy as their choice.

The very fact that most medical schools set the study of the anatomy of the brain and nervous system aside into a separate category would suggest that somehow it is a more complex and impenetrable study than the anatomy of other systems.

In many respects it is. There are many different kinds of nervous tissue making up the brain and nervous system, yet all nervous tissue looks very much the same. Arteries and veins are easy to trace out from source to end; they are easy to separate and identify. But the fibers of a motor nerve look exactly like the fibers of a sensory nerve, and the portions of the brain with which they connect look practically identical— yet the functions of the two kinds of nerves are as different as night and day.

Further confusion arises from the fact that the anatomy of the nervous system is replete with hundreds of names for structures which have no counterpart elsewhere in the body. The student must learn to recognize boundary lines and structures which he can barely distinguish either grossly or microscopically.

Neuroanatomy seems all the more formidable to the student because here, at least, he can readily understand its importance. Just as a breakdown in one place in a complex electrical system will produce "symptoms" in a remote part and only in that part, so disturbances in the nervous system are identifiable to such a specific degree that the physician who is well grounded in neuroanatomy can very readily pinpoint, or "localize," the place where the disturbance is by observing the symptoms and signs. No other organ system in the body shows such a reliable cause-and-effect relationship, or aids so much in diagnosis.

Thus neuroanatomy deserves a slightly special place, and perhaps even deserves the extra respect of medical students. Still, there is no reason that it should overawe you. As with all anatomy, the structure of the nervous system is complex but entirely logical. It may require a bit more work, and seem a bit more confusing, but it will come clear if it is taken a step at a time.

Throughout your work in anatomy you will be asking yourself, "How will I be able to use this information? Is it really important to know so much detail? Or will I be learning it simply to forget it next year?" It seems to be quite the vogue among medical students to be a bit contemptuous of "minutiae"—the myriad tiny details they seem to be expected to know and understand.

But the importance of minutiae will become clear when you stand at the operating table and see the extreme anatomical detail the surgeon needs to know in order to perform his operations safely and well. There are no details of anatomy that will not be useful to you, as a physician, at one time or another in your career. What is more, you will continue to learn more and more details as long as you are active in the practice of medicine.

One thing which is helpful to remember in anatomy, and very easy to lose sight of, is the fact that there is a limit to the amount to be learned. It is easy to be overwhelmed by the staggering number of details to be memorized, remembered, recognized, and brought to mind. To the first-year student it may appear that there is no end to what must be learned; how can he hope to learn more than a tiny fraction of it?

Probably he will not learn more than that—but the total amount to be learned is not limitless. Every structure of the body is part of one or another organ system. There are a limited number of systems: the bony framework of the body, the muscular system, the cardiovascular system, the respiratory system, the digestive system, the skin and fascia, and so forth.

You will not learn all there is to know about the structure of any one of those systems—but you will learn a great deal about each in first-year anatomy. You will continue to add to that basic knowledge throughout your professional life. But everything will fall into one system or another; there is a limit.

Physiology: The Way the Machinery Works

You may be somewhat relieved to learn that much of the material you will encounter in physiology will be at least partly familiar.

Physiology is the study of the function of the organ systems of the body in making a living, breathing human being. Since you are just that—a living, breathing human being—you have in a sense been studying practical physiology all your life. You have been a walking physiology laboratory. So you will start physiology with a broad personal experience in precisely what a normal human body—your own—can or cannot do.

What you will learn now is how and why it can or cannot do these things.

Here again laboratory is important, but in physiology lecture is almost equally important. A great deal of physiology is theory, things which might be provable in the laboratory but which would take too long or require too much specialized equipment. In laboratory you will see some of the capabilities and limitations of the human body, but your lectures will help you very much to understand why.

You will study respiration and circulation, digestion and excretion. You will give each other basal metabolism tests and learn how to record electrocardiograms (although it may be years before you learn how to read them satisfactorily). You will study many wonderful and mysterious mechanisms that regulate body functions—for example, the mechanisms which regulate the maintenance of normal blood pressure. No one yet has devised a laboratory mechanism that can duplicate the way the body regulates the pressure of blood in the arteries and veins, although a dozen such devices have been built. You will learn what things keep the blood pressure up, and what happens to the body when it goes down.

Many of your observations in physiology will be made directly upon yourself and your classmates. I was elected by my laboratory partners to swallow a small rubber balloon on the end of a tube so that my gastric motility could be measured. Since I had to remain utterly calm and composed all afternoon while my partners took readings and made pressure graphs, I brought a mystery novel to read. It was a pretty exciting mystery novel, and I still have the graph showing the on-the-spot effect of "The Screaming Mimi" on my gastrointestinal tract while I read it.

Biochemistry: The Chemistry of Living Creatures

If physiology represents the "gross" function of the human body, biochemistry can be considered the study of the "microscopic" function. Life begins and ends in the individual cells as a result of chemical reactions occurring there. In biochemistry you will study many of those reactions in detail.

Here your background in college chemistry is your greatest friend. Chemical reactions are chemical reactions, whether they occur in a laboratory beaker or in a living cell. The only difference is that reactions occurring in the living cell are more complex.

You will spend many hours in laboratory studying enzyme reactions and metabolic processes. You will learn the part that various organs play in the living processes, or metabolism, of the body. You will also begin to see how malfunction of certain of these processes can cause major breakdowns in the normal working of the body—the condition we know as "disease." Much of biochemistry, like any chemistry, involves complex formulae and confusing reaction chains—but here at last you have something positive to relate these formulae and reactions to.

You will learn what proteins, carbohydrates, and fats are, and how they are taken into the body and converted into the building blocks that sustain life. You will study the pH of the blood, and learn the delicate way it is balanced in all body fluids. Biochemistry takes its toll of medical students just as organic chemistry takes its toll of premedical students, but even the slowest student can see why an understanding of biochemistry is absolutely necessary to the understanding of sickness and health, or of diagnosis and cure.

Special Problems in the First Year

As a freshman medical student you will have some special problems and decisions to make. Oftentimes advice about such things as microscopes, textbooks, examinations, and failures is given all too freely; I will try to stick to practical considerations in discussing a few of the questions which will arise.

YOUR MICROSCOPE. You will need one during your freshman year, probably from the start, so this is one detail you would be wise to take care of in the summer before classes begin.

Your microscope will represent a significant investment of money; what is more, you will need an instrument which you can trust to work properly whenever you need it. Nothing can be more maddening in microanatomy than a microscope which is constantly on the verge of falling apart on the table. You will be wise to take time and exercise caution in selecting yours.

Some schools allow students to rent microscopes for use in the first year. If you are an expert on microscopes and how they work you may get away less expensively by renting one. If not, be very careful. Rental microscopes are too frequently old, overused, misused, and in poor repair. The ratchet sticks, or else it moves too freely. The scope will not stay in focus properly; perhaps a lens is cracked or dirty on the inside where you can't get at it to clean it. You end up spending too much precious time fighting your microscope and too little time examining slides. This is not always the case, by any means, but it happens often enough that you should be forewarned.

It is usually better to buy a microscope—either a new one or a used instrument that has been cleaned, overhauled, and reconditioned by its maker. Any microscope you buy should have the standard three objectives, including an oil-emersion objective and a 10X eyepiece.

Binocular microscopes are popular because they are supposed to be easier on your eyes over long hours of use. Maybe so; I used a monocular scope all through medical school and I still have perfect eyesight. A binocular eyepiece will add from $100 to $300 to the cost of your instrument, so you will have to decide whether the comfort and convenience are worth the price.

New American-made instruments cost from $600 to $800 at current prices. Many German microscopes are on the market at similar prices. A used or reconditioned instrument may cost you only half as much as a new one—but be sure you are 100 per cent satisfied with the way it works before you buy it.

In recent years the Japanese have made some excellent microscopes, and these are often available at very significant savings: prices ranging from $300 to $500. These are well-made optical instruments, and you need not be concerned with poor workmanship if you buy a well-known make such as the Yashima instrument.

In any event, be sure to check the specifications of your particular medical school with regard to microscopes. Most schools will allow any major-name three-ocular microscope which is in good condition. Your instrument should be equipped with a sliding stage for easy manipulation of slides on the stage. This accessory costs extra, but it pays for itself in convenience.

PASSING AND FAILING. All through your first year you will hear horrible tales about the danger of flunking out of medical school. These stories will sound much the same as the ones you heard in premedicine. You will hear that one school flunked thirty students from their first-year class, and that another deliberately admits more freshmen than it can accommodate in its second-year class, and so on, and so on.

Most of what you hear just isn't true. If you are really worried, talk to upperclassmen in your own school and ask them what percentage of their classes failed in the first year.

You will probably find that the percentage was very low.

After all, there must have been some point to the careful selectivity the medical schools used in filling their freshman classes. It costs a medical school money to teach a student for a year and then drop him. Most schools try to do their weeding out before a freshman class begins; they feel that with rare exceptions the students they finally admit are of doctor caliber and can handle the work.

So most medical schools are eager, if possible, to graduate every student they admit to their freshman classes. They realize that worrying about failing actually steals valuable study time and rest time from their students. They seek to do everything they can to eliminate it.

Nevertheless, some will fail for one reason or another. A student carrying a burden of part-time work on the side is in serious danger. He just will not have time enough for studying. Occasionally there is a lazy one who finds that the work expected of him is just more than he wants to do—not that he can't do it, just that he won't.

Again, an occasional student finds that the work is over his head. Perhaps he is slow-learning, or just too doggedly methodical in his study habits; maybe he hasn't learned yet how to concentrate, or reads a little too slowly. These are things that can frequently be corrected with the aid of tutors, or with severe self-application, but sometimes they overwhelm the student and he doesn't make the grade.

Health also is a factor. Every medical school loses an occasional student to tuberculosis. Long working hours, too little rest, the possibility that the disease was present but unrecognized to start with or was contracted in contact with patients —it's tragic, but it happens. Another "medical student's disease" is regional enteritis. Here emotional disturbances, worry, and tension play a part.

Every student in medical school must regard his health seriously, for it can ruin a promising medical career as rapidly as anything else if something goes wrong.

COMPETITION. The battle for grades will carry over into medical school even when there is no logical reason for it. Too many students have gotten into the "competition habit" in college. In medical school they waste a great deal of energy in competition which might better be spent studying anatomy.

Of course there are exams, and often, in the first year. They may be difficult. The faculty wants to keep the students on their toes. But if you have kept up with your work, without falling behind, and have worked honestly and diligently on a day-by-day basis, you will pass the exams. You have one job: to learn as much anatomy and physiology and biochemistry as you can pack in during the time allotted. You may not bring down straight A's, but you'll pass muster.

TEXTBOOKS. You might as well be prepared in advance to be shocked the first time you walk into the medical bookstore.

It has been said that everything you ever buy in connection with medicine will cost you twice as much as a comparable item not associated with medicine.

It certainly seems true with textbooks.

You will want the newest, latest-edition textbook in any of the courses you are taking. These books will become part of your permanent medical library; you will use them again and again, and probably replace them when new editions are published. This means buying books new, and not selling them until they are quite out-of-date.

But the prices!

Average price for a major textbook (anatomy, physiology, biochemistry, etc.) is currently between $15 and $20. Going up every year.

Minor texts run $8 to $12. Also going up.

Certain pamphlets and paper-bound books you will need will cost $3 to $5.

Expensive, yes, but here is one place to go whole hog. Don't try to skimp on your books. You depend upon them too much. Even though it means an annual outlay approaching $100 for books alone, it is worth it.

Many students are confused because there always seem to be two different textbooks to choose between. Which one is better? In anatomy, for instance, you will want either the Morris or the Gray. Which one should you buy?

Sometimes your instructors will go out on a limb and tell you which they recommend in any given course. Usually each book will have certain advantages and certain disadvantages. Talk to upper-class students who have used each, and draw your own conclusions before you buy. You can't go too far wrong—the other book will always be available in the medical library if you need it.

What about Medical Fraternities?

If you belonged to a college social fraternity you will be surprised by the differences you find in the medical fraternities.

Like fraternities in college, those in medical school are social fraternities—places where students live, eat, make friends, and associate as a group, with a social calendar, promoting congenial relations among the men who are its members. But medical fraternities are different in ways that count.

Everybody in the medical fraternity has a job to do, and knows it. That job is to study medicine. Everything else, including social activities and horseplay around the house, comes second. The emphasis is on scholarship and getting the work done.

Study hours are established and enforced. There are no pledge duties and no "hell week"; for one thing, the freshmen don't have the time and, for another, these are essentially childish things that have been put aside to make way for a man's work—studying medicine.

In most medical schools there are enough fraternities to accommodate all the students who are interested in joining. Fraternities are an additional expense, yet many houses help students finance themselves by providing "house jobs" for meals and lodging.

Here, as in college, you can decide for yourself whether fraternity life is for you or not. Many students feel, however, that in medical fraternities the advantages of fraternity living are emphasized while most of the disadvantages are done away with. College fraternities might well take a lesson from them.

If the first year of medical school sounds like a lot of hard work from the description above, rest assured that it is. When you finish your last final exam in June you will know you've been through a year of medical school. But you have two rewards to look forward to:

First, you have the knowledge that, once through the first year, the odds are 98 per cent favorable that you will ultimately get through medical school. You have lots of work ahead of you, but the big hurdles are behind. You will be back in September a seasoned veteran, wondering if you looked as lost the year before as the new freshmen do.

Second, you have a whole summer ahead to forget textbooks and pretend you don't know what "laboratory" means.

Time enough for that in September!

NINE

Medical School: The Second Year

EVEN THOUGH THE first year's work laid the groundwork for what comes later, it probably did not give you much of the "feel" of studying medicine. It was too much like the junior or senior year of premedicine, though more intense and specialized. If you felt that way, you can be certain that the second year will be very different.

This is still a "preclinical" year; that is, you will not yet be concerned primarily with sick patients in the hospital. Nevertheless, this second year of medical school takes you into the heart of your medical studies.

You will have to work at least as hard as before, often harder, but now the subject matter will seem far more exciting. In the second year you will be learning about the development and progress of disease in the human body.

Now, perhaps for the first time, you will begin to see clearly how important it is to know the normal structure and function of the body, for you will begin to study the thousands of abnormalities and disorders which bring so much pain and misery to human beings, and which are the reason that physicians exist at all.

This study of abnormalities and disorders of the human body is called *pathology*. In the older textbooks it used to be called "morbid anatomy" but this is a gloomy term, and not at all accurate, so it has been discarded. Pathology will swallow up the lion's share of your time in the second year.

Side by side with pathology you will work in *bacteriology*, the study of the microorganisms which invade the human body to cause disease. The new antibiotic drugs have not made bacteriology any less important in a doctor's training; on the contrary, as we will see, it is even more important than it used to be. Bacterial diseases still remain a constant threat and a potential killer in our world today in spite of all the progress that has been made fighting them.

But the word "medicine" implies more than the diagnosis of illness; it also implies treatment. Your study of *pharmacology* will acquaint you with a multitude of drugs and medicinal substances which affect the function of the body both in sickness and in health.

These "preclinical" sciences will complete the theoretical groundwork for your study and practice of medicine. But you will need certain very practical *clinical* tools before you can proceed with your work with patients. The first step in dealing with a sick person is to try to discover what is wrong with him. First, you must take his medical history, asking questions about his present illness and learning anything that might be helpful about his past state of health. Second, you must examine him to see what, if anything, you can discover to be abnormal. Finally, you must conduct certain laboratory studies to aid you further in discovering the nature of his illness.

Each of these three steps requires a knowledge of very specialized techniques. A portion of your second year will be devoted to teaching you these techniques in your courses in physical diagnosis and laboratory diagnosis.

Finally, you will attend a number of introductory clinical lectures in medicine, surgery, pediatrics, and other branches of medicine. These lectures will further prepare you for the full-time clinical work to come in the third year.

Pathology: The Keystone of Medicine

The medical dictionary defines *pathology* as "that branch of medicine which treats of the essential nature of disease, especially of the structural and functional changes which cause or are caused by disease."

From this definition it is obvious why pathology must be

the keystone upon which our entire understanding of medicine depends.

First, it is concerned with the "essential nature of disease" —not just how disease is manifested, or how it feels to the patient, but what it is. Second, it is concerned particularly with the changes in the body which are associated with disease.

Obviously, pathology would be a waste of time if you did not have a solid understanding of the normal structure and function of the various parts of the human body. But, once you have that background, what you learn in pathology will be the basis for everything else you learn in medicine.

More than that—pathology is fascinating.

After all, what is "illness"? How does it come about? What forms can it take, and how does it reveal its presence? How does it affect the normal life of an individual? What is the significance of the "symptoms" of illness—often the only outward and visible signs that something, somewhere, has gone wrong? How can you tell, from the "symptoms," just what the "illness" is?

This is your job as a physician.

All through medical school you will find the emphasis is placed on diagnosis, not on treatment. Any physician can learn, from one source or another, how to treat an illness once he knows what illness he is dealing with. But, until he knows that, he is helpless to do anything but treat the symptoms, and you will learn in pathology that the symptoms are not, by any means, the disease.

You may be wondering how you can hope to learn in one year all there is to know about all the diseases the human body can fall victim to. It is easy to be discouraged by the apparent vastness of the ground to be covered. How can you hope to cover it all?

The answer is, of course, that you can't. But here again the limitations we spoke of come into play. We know, from the first year, that there are only a limited number of organs and organ systems in the body. Similarly, there is a limited number of types of things that can go wrong. In each type of disorder there may be endless variations and differences—indeed, every patient you see will present an individual variation, and you soon learn that there is no such thing as a "typical," or "textbook," case of any illness—but the classes of illness are limited in number.

In pathology you will learn these broad classes of disease, and the patterns of change in the body that go with them. You will spend the rest of your medical lives learning the variations and details; at present what you need is a skeleton of information about disease upon which to build detail as you go along.

This is why medical journals are so important to practicing physicians. Hardly an issue of the *American Heart Journal* appears but there is an article discussing angina pectoris. This symptom—a characteristic type of pain associated with heart disease—has been recognized almost as long as men have been writing things down, yet physicians are still learning more about it. As more is learned, new articles are written for other physicians to read. Understand that this is not a journal that a medical student will be likely to read; it is read regularly by physicians who have been practicing medicine and treating heart disease for forty years. They are still adding details to their skeleton of knowledge about disease.

Nevertheless, the amount which must be learned to form the skeleton for later learning is still pretty staggering. How do you go about learning it in second-year medical school?

First, you have lectures. In many medical schools the finest lectures and lecturers will be found in the department of pathology. Here you will learn about general physical reactions—such as inflammation, a response of the body to irritating stimuli—and then later about specific diseases. In some cases the diseases are limited to a single organ: pneumonia, for example. In other cases the disease process may involve many organ systems: cancer, for instance, or the disorders known as "collagen diseases" because they affect connective tissue in all organs of the body.

With all the lectures you will study a textbook of pathology, the thickest, heaviest, most difficult of all your medical textbooks. You will spend many hours in the pathology laboratory. This lab resembles microanatomy lab, for here you examine "tissue sections," prepared slides made of thin slices of diseased tissue. By comparing diseased tissue with normal tissue you can actually see the microscopic changes that occur in disease. You will see, for example, what changes occur in the lung during the course of pneumonia. You will see how these changes can account for the symptoms the patient will describe and the physical changes you will be able to detect during your examination of the patient.

In contrast, you will see the far-flung changes that occur throughout the body in patients suffering from hypertension, or high blood pressure. This is a generalized disease affecting many organs; it is easy to see why it is such an elusive disorder to deal with, since symptoms can arise from any one or a combination of sources.

Again, you will learn the differences between normal healthy tissue and the wild, disordered growth of cells that we know as cancer. You will understand how, by its pattern of growth alone, it can often be a far-advanced disease before the patient notices any symptoms at all.

There are other ways you will learn pathology, along with lectures, textbook, and slide examination. In the second year you will attend your first autopsies (often called "post-mortem examinations" or "posts"). Medical students sometimes call the hospital morgue the "temple of truth" because here, indeed, the answers are found. Why did the patient die? Were we entirely right, partly right, or completely wrong in our diagnosis? Was the disease farther advanced than we suspected? If so, why didn't we know it? Did we do the right thing when we treated the patient? Could we have done more? The autopsy may not answer all these questions, but it will answer many of them.

You will also examine "fresh pathology" specimens brought to the pathology lab from the operating rooms of the hospital. Perhaps the specimen one day will be a portion of stomach removed from a patient with a preoperative diagnosis of "gastric ulcer"; but you can see from the specimen that the "ulcer" is in fact a cancer. At first it will be hard to make "pathological diagnosis" on an isolated specimen, especially if you can't even tell for sure which organ it is, but gradually you will learn.

Finally, you will study the preserved specimens kept in the pathological museum. Sometimes these are merely oddities.

One item that intrigued my class was the cervix of a hippopotamus, kept preserved in a huge bell jar. But usually the specimens here are "normal abnormalities" which you will be somewhat more likely to encounter in your practice of medicine.

In addition to the formal ways that pathology is taught, you will learn by talk and discussion with your colleagues. This is a casual way to learn, but an extremely important one. You stop for a coffee break in the middle of a long morning over the microscope, and talk pathology. At lunch and at supper you talk pathology. Differences of opinion begin to appear, for nothing in pathology is quite so cut and dried as in anatomy and microanatomy, and you begin to learn the hardest, most disillusioning lesson of all: that doctors don't know all the answers.

You will not be a really good doctor until you have learned that lesson more thoroughly than any other.

Bacteriology: An Undying Field

In recent years medical students have taken a rather patronizing attitude toward bacteriology.

They don't exactly sneer at it. Its history in the development of medicine is too long and star-studded for that. But they do tend to laugh up their sleeves a little when they see bacteriology scheduled as one of their second-year courses. After all, don't we have antibiotic drugs now? Why get so excited about a dying field in medicine? Bacterial diseases are a thing of the past; why worry about them now?

In a small town in New Jersey not long ago a laboratory technician grew a culture from a little girl's sore throat and reported to her doctor that he had found *Corynebacterium diphtheriae* present. The doctor scoffed; there hadn't been a case of diphtheria in town for fifteen years. He ordered a repeat culture, but before it had a chance to grow the little girl had a membrane in her throat and was having trouble breathing. That child survived—but a year or two later a college girl in a Western city died of diphtheria because her doctor had not thought a throat culture necessary, and was treating her "tonsillitis" with the wrong antibiotic.

Diphtheria is a thing of the past? Not quite. Neither is tuberculosis. Neither is typhoid fever. Neither are a hundred other killers of the past that could—and would—be killers of the present if doctors lowered their guard or forgot their bacteriology. Far from disappearing, bacterial diseases are a constant shadow at the physician's elbow. And that shadow will still be there a thousand years from now—antibiotics or no antibiotics.

During my internship an eight-year-old boy was admitted to the hospital in shock and almost dead. He had a stiff neck, and hundreds of tiny red pin points covering his legs and thighs. We confirmed our suspicions by making a stained smear of a sample of spinal fluid—meningococcal meningitis. We worked for sixteen long hard hours before we were reasonably confident that that boy was not going to die of meningitis the first day in the hospital. We didn't feel so casual about bacterial diseases that day.

It is true, of course, that antibiotics have changed things. They have saved many lives, and added much to our knowledge. But there is something very strange about new knowledge in medicine. It never seems to make things simpler. For every answer that is found five new questions always seem to arise. New avenues of research are opened. Doctors discover that things they formerly thought were simple and straightforward are actually far more complex than they dreamed.

Take antibiotics and pneumonia, for example. Time was when a patient with pneumonia was put to bed, given a sponge bath or two, and not much else. He either recovered or he didn't, depending upon how strong his body was otherwise. Not a very satisfactory way to deal with a dangerous disease, I admit.

Then someone discovered how to make antisera against the different types of pneumococci causing pneumonia. When a case of pneumonia appeared, it was necessary to find out which of seventy-seven different types of pneumococci was causing it, and use the right antiserum to combat it. Things were getting more complex, but more people were surviving pneumonia.

Then came the golden drug, sulfanilamide. It killed all types of pneumococci, just like that. End of problem? Not quite. It also killed a certain number of patients who might have survived without it. The drug had some poisonous side effects. And some pneumonias just didn't respond—why not?

The sulfa drugs were improved, made less toxic and thus safer to use. Then along came penicillin, wonderfully safe except for allergic reactions. But how much to use? When to use it? What about the pneumonias caused by bacteria that penicillin will not kill? What about the growing numbers of bacteria that develop resistance to penicillin?

We are living in a world filled with potentially dangerous bacteria. How can we protect ourselves against them if the doctors don't know what harm they can do, and how to stop them? Bacteriology has changed in that there is much more to be learned. There are a dozen antibiotic agents with individual qualities to be memorized. There are diagnostic procedures and programs of therapy which must become part of your knowledge of medicine. You will learn them in bacteriology.

Pharmacology

A generation ago medical students took a course called "materia medica" in which they spent much time memorizing prescriptions that they would use in their practice of medicine.

Today in a modern pharmacology course you may not memorize a single prescription, but you will learn a great deal about drugs and how they affect normal—and abnormal—human bodies.

Pharmacology is usually taught in experimental laboratory. You will use animals in measuring the effect of drugs on living creatures. Sometimes the animal you use will be yourself; at other times you will use dogs, or rabbits, or guinea pigs.

There will be lectures, but in pharmacology it is most important that you actually observe and measure the changes which occur. It is much more effective to observe, on the spot, what happens when an excessive amount of potassium solution is administered to an animal than merely to hear that it makes the heart stop beating. Before very long you will be prescribing intravenous solutions for hospital patients, which contain small amounts of potassium solution; it's better that you should learn on a dog firsthand how much is too much before you begin treating patients.

Obviously you can't hope to understand drug effects on the body unless you understand normal physiology, so part of pharmacology will be a review of what is normal. This illustrates another great truth about learning to be a doctor: You will forget much that you learn. Your medical training is a process of repeating and repeating and repeating the things which are important to know. Even as you review physiology when you study pharmacology, so you will later review both physiology and pharmacology as you learn clinical medicine.

This process of reviewing and repetition never ceases. The surgeon who has been practicing surgery for twenty years may still be found, the night before an important operation, reviewing once again the anatomy of the region in which he will be working. It isn't that he doesn't know the anatomy—it is just that he knows that he will be reminded afresh that this nerve runs here, and must be protected, and that this blood vessel can be safely cut here, but if cut there he will have trouble on his hands.

Physical Diagnosis: Your Introduction to Clinical Medicine

With the courses we have discussed above you will complete your groundwork in the basic medical sciences. You will know a great deal—theoretically, at least—about the human body in illness and in health.

But you still are not ready to step into a hospital and make much sense of what you see there.

There are certain practical techniques you must learn before you can approach a patient and make a diagnosis. These are the techniques of physical diagnosis and medical history taking.

Here you will truly feel that you are becoming a doctor. You will go into the hospital certain mornings during the week and make rounds on the wards with your instructor, an experienced physician. You will wear your white clinical jacket and learn to carry your new stethoscope in one pocket and your ophthalmoscope in another so that neither of them falls out. You will begin to examine patients, and hear yourself called "doctor" by a patient for the first time. You may even have to squelch your impulse to reply, "Oh, but I'm not a doctor, really."

But you will not say that, because during these hours, and to these patients, you are indeed a doctor and nothing else.

What is a physical examination? How do you examine a patient to discover physical manifestations of illness, and what do you look for? The first time you listen to a patient's chest through a stethoscope you will hear a great deal of noise, but most of it will come from scraping the stethoscope across his skin, and not from what's happening inside. How do you pick out the important sounds, and what do they mean?

It is only by practice that you will learn to recognize *râles* when you hear them, to distinguish a "wheeze" from a "normal breath sound." You will need practice to recognize the different parts of heart sounds, and still more to detect the characteristic sound of a "murmur." Weeks may pass before you learn the difference in sound and feel of "resonance" and "dullness" when you thump a patient's chest with your finger. Gradually you will learn to feel—and know for sure that you feel—the edge of a patient's liver or spleen with your fingers, or to detect a mass in the abdomen where no mass ought to be.

The importance of performing careful, complete physical examinations can't be exaggerated. Very recently a medical colleague was telling me of a patient who had come to his office, a twenty-six-year-old man who complained of a slight chest cold. He looked like a healthy young fellow, and his chest sounded normal through the stethoscope. But my doctor friend was thorough; he thought he detected one tiny area in the patient's chest that sounded a trifle too dull when he tapped it with his finger. "I couldn't be sure, and it worried me a little," the doctor said. "It was only an area the size of a quarter, but I took a chest X ray just the same."

"What did you find?" I asked.

"We operated on the man this morning," the doctor replied, "and removed an early carcinoma."

This was astute physical diagnosis. Many doctors would have missed it. But when that patient went to his doctor he assumed that if anything were wrong the doctor would find it. Thanks to that doctor's careful examination, the man may have sixty more years to live instead of the two or three he might have had if the cancer had not been spotted on that first visit.

You will learn physical diagnosis by examining patients—hundreds and thousands of patients—with care and patience and attention to the tiniest detail. You begin this learning process on physical diagnosis rounds in your second year.

You will also learn the art of medical history taking. Dr. O. H. Perry Pepper at the University of Pennsylvania often told his students, "Listen to the patient; he is telling you his diagnosis." You may not understand what the patient is saying, of course. He doesn't know medical terms. Much that he tells you may be irrelevant. But you must, somehow, find out from the patient what bothers him—where he hurts, how he feels sick, what doesn't seem right to him.

Again, practice is important in taking medical histories and recording them. You will write your histories in longhand at the time, or just after, you take them. As a medical student your histories may be many pages long and still miss important points. Later, with experience, you can condense them to four or five pages. As an intern you will record everything of significance in a page and a half or two pages. When you are practicing medicine your histories may be only three paragraphs long. But they are all the same medical history. In your second year you start learning to record accurate histories. You will never stop learning.

Fortunately, the doctor has an additional aid in making his diagnosis besides history and physical examination. Modern laboratory studies often provide critical information about the state of a patient's health. In your second year you will become acquainted with many of the most useful laboratory studies: blood counts, urinalysis, spinal fluid examination, etc. Few diagnoses depend solely upon the results of laboratory studies; however, few diagnoses are made without their assistance.

Clinical Lectures

Finally, your second year will bring you in contact with another form of medical teaching: the clinical lecture. Doctors from the hospital will give introductory lectures in medicine, surgery, pediatrics, psychiatry, and other branches of medicine. This first taste of "medical teaching" will give you a good feeling. You will find yourself looking forward with great eagerness to the next year's work, your first "clinical year."

If it seems that the second year will be excessively busy, at least you will have no new special problems to deal with. Textbooks are as before—expensive, heavy, difficult to read. You will buy your stethoscope, if you haven't received one for Christmas (this is a favorite gift for medical students, it seems). Another specialized instrument you will need is the combination of ophthalmoscope (eye-looker) and otoscope (ear-looker). You will require a rubber reflex hammer and a few other accessories, and may wish to invest in a small Gladstone bag to carry them in. We called these second-year instruments our "boy-doctor toys" and they seemed very much like toys at first. Gradually they became so much a part of us that we felt quite strange going out on a Saturday night date without our stethoscopes in our pockets!

But hard as it is to think of yourself as a doctor at this point, in your third year you will become a doctor in your own thinking. That is the time when you step into quite a different way of learning how to be a doctor. . . .

By being one.

TEN

Medical School:
The Third Year

THIRD YEAR!

Things will really be different now. Not only will you be doing a different kind of work, but your own attitude toward your work will be changing constantly through your third year of medical school.

Until now it has been hard to feel that you were becoming a doctor. Even on physical diagnosis rounds, when you were learning how to behave the way a doctor behaves, you were plagued with the feeling that it was some kind of masquerade which you would have to maintain when you walked in the front door of the hospital at the beginning of the third year.

Now that the time has come you are still wondering. You have your white clinical jacket on; your stethoscope is lodged in your side pocket quite professionally. You have received your first ward assignment—Ward D, perhaps, Medical, with instructions to report to Dr. Ex, who is the ward chief there, and to Drs. Wy and Zee, the resident and intern on the ward.

You realize that you are leaving classrooms and laboratories behind you, and that you will be working with those strange and somehow terrifying creatures known as patients, although you don't know just how you're going to be working with them. All the time you are wondering what you are doing there pretending to be a doctor when you know that you're not one even if nobody else seems to realize it. . . .

Well, maybe. On the other hand, you may be feeling too

excited to be thinking about anything except how to get up the hospital steps without stumbling.

You're right, of course. You aren't a doctor yet. Not quite. There actually isn't any clear-cut point at which you cease to be a "medical student" and begin to be a "doctor." You aren't even certain, at this point, exactly what a doctor is.

But at some point or another you do begin to be a doctor, and the change for most medical students takes place sometime in the course of their third year.

How can you tell when the bridge is crossed? I don't know. It's a completely personal matter. It may occur when you first begin doing the things in a hospital that a doctor does, even if you know you are only copying what the interns and residents are doing. Perhaps it happens when you first accept some degree of medical responsibility, however slight, in the ward or surgery, and realize with a sudden shock that this patient's welfare depends upon you to some extent. But somewhere along the line you will realize in your heart that you not only can be a doctor, and want to be one, but that you actually have become one.

I can't tell you when it will happen to you; I can only tell you when it happened to me. I was in my third-year section on surgery, assigned to a surgical ward in the hospital and "working up" patients that came in for surgery. I took histories and performed physical examinations on the patients just as if I were the surgical resident responsible, recording my findings on the patients' charts.

One day I examined a middle-aged lady who had come to her doctor because she thought she had detected a lump in her right breast. Her doctor agreed that there was a lump that shouldn't be there. The lump was to be biopsied to see if it were cancer; if so, the breast would have to be removed.

She had been seen by her doctor, by the surgical resident, and by the intern. Each one had recorded the same finding: a small mass in the upper outer quadrant of the right breast. But I, as a student, was not supposed to read the patient's chart. I was expected to determine from my own history and examination what I thought the diagnosis might be. I did so, and I also discovered a lump in the patient's breast—the left breast.

The intern thought I had written "left" when I meant "right," and ignored it. The surgical resident was more wary; he checked my findings and contacted the patient's doctor. Next morning both breasts were biopsied. The lump on the right was a perfectly harmless cyst; the one on the left was an early carcinoma. I was "hero for the day" and it was on that day that I knew I had stopped being a medical student and had started being a doctor.

Almost all your work with patients in the third year will be practice work. You will not have much responsibility. You will cover ground that has already been covered by several fully qualified physicians, and they will check you every step of the way. You will blunder, and be corrected, and blunder again. With each blunder you will learn something; as time goes by things will begin to form a pattern in your mind and you will blunder less and less frequently.

Classwork will not be over. You will attend dozens of lectures in clinical medicine. You will attend recitation classes with regular textbook reading assignments. You will take exams. You will do laboratory work required by your patients, attend X-ray drill conferences, study electrocardiograms. But now your attention will be directed entirely at the sick patient in the hospital.

Your third-year work will be split into certain very clear-cut sections.

You will spend long periods of time working on medical wards and surgical wards. There will be shorter periods in the children's ward, or pediatrics; in obstetrics, working in the labor room and the delivery room; in psychiatry, studying the care of the mentally ill. Throughout the year you will begin, in the classical sense, "reading medicine" side by side with your practical experience with hospital patients.

This work will be entirely with "inpatients," people sick enough to be hospitalized for their illnesses. You will see patients who are hardly sick at all, and patients who are extremely ill; there will be patients with long-term, chronic illness, and others with acute illnesses. You will see death occur, just as you will witness miraculous recoveries.

In every sense of the word you will be studying medicine.

You will find that the textbooks are no longer so precise

and dogmatic in their statements. In your textbooks of medicine or surgery you will see that much simply is not known, and much is poorly understood. These texts are often difficult to read. They do not say "first you have this and then you have that." Instead, they are more likely to say "in certain cases this will appear, and when it does 7 per cent of the patients will do this, 23 per cent will do this, and the rest will probably do thus-and-so."

The "clinical manifestations" of a disease may be far different from what you would expect in light of the pathological changes. You will learn more and more that the total amount that is known in medicine is far smaller than the total amount that is *not* known. This, too, is part of studying medicine.

The Medical Wards

At least one-third of your time in third year is spent on the "medical wards" learning "medicine."

Here the terms "medical" and "medicine" are used in a very limited sense. The medical dictionary defines "medicine" in the broad sense as "the art or science of healing diseases" —and then follows this broad definition with a more limited meaning: "especially the healing of diseases by administration of internal remedies."

In this sense the word "medicine" is used in contrast to "surgery"—the branch of medicine which treats diseases, wholly or in part, by operative procedure. Likewise, we speak of "medical cases" as opposed to "surgical cases," and "medical diagnosis" as distinguished from "surgical diagnosis."

Of course this is an artificial distinction. Both "medical" patients and "surgical" patients are ill in one way or another. Frequently a patient comes to the hospital with a "medical" diagnosis, and ends up being treated surgically. But the breakdown is useful to divide the immense field of work which is medicine into units that can be conveniently handled —and taught.

Any division of hospital care is spoken of as a "service." Thus your months on the "medical service" will be spent working with patients who are not likely to be treated operatively, but by the administration of drugs and medicines. The division is made according to the type of symptoms the patient presents, and his probable diagnosis.

The patients on the medical wards are most frequently the "diagnostic problems." As a third-year student—"extern"— you will work closely with the hospital house staff of interns and residents assigned to the medical wards. Much of your work will be "copy-work." That is, you will do complete admission work-ups on the patients assigned to you, including medical histories and physical examinations of the patients, although your work-ups will not be official. You will be expected to decide what you think is wrong with the patient— not just the one thing that may seem most likely, but all the things which you think might possibly account for the trouble. You will be expected to recommend laboratory studies you would like to confirm your suspicions, to suggest appropriate treatment for the patient, and to record how you think the patient should respond. These things you will put down in writing. In most hospitals your work-ups do not become part of the permanent hospital record. On some occasions, however, they do, especially in hospitals where the student's history is the only history taken when the patient is admitted.

In doing work-ups of this sort you are doing exactly what the intern and resident do when a patient is admitted to their care. Their work-ups will be recorded on the patient's chart, as will their orders for lab studies and their recommendations for treatment. This does not mean, however, that your work-up is superfluous. As a student—believe it or not—you will have far more time to spend with each patient than an overworked intern or a busy resident has. Your medical history may be incomplete because of your inexperience, but you may also put your finger on aspects of the patient's history that everyone else has missed. Not infrequently medical students come up with the right diagnosis when it has been missed by the house staff, or the attending physician.

The reason for this is not hard to understand. In most cases when a medical patient is admitted to the hospital his diagnosis is in question. Sometimes patients are admitted solely for diagnostic work-ups. In such cases a number of different diagnoses may explain part of the picture, and the doctor must decide which is the most likely before he begins treatment. The different possibilities to be considered are called the "differential diagnosis."

Often laboratory studies will help to rule out certain possibilities and make others seem more likely. Sometimes the way the illness develops in the hospital makes the diagnosis clear, and all too often the true diagnosis never is established and proved for sure. But everyone who sees the patient, from the medical student right up to the chief of the medical service, puts down what he thinks—in writing. Every possible idea is considered carefully, and almost invariably the more heads working on the problem the better.

Once a patient has been worked up, you will be responsible for following his progress in the hospital. You will see your patients—and other patients—several times during the day, on rounds. You will make "business rounds" with the intern, reviewing each patient's chart, noting new laboratory findings, observing changes in the patient as he responds to treatment. There will also be "teaching rounds" with your ward chief, in which you will discuss the medical problems of certain patients in detail. Business rounds are for the care of the patient; teaching rounds are for the medical student. On both kinds of rounds you will learn to recognize physical changes in the patient, and to connect physical findings, laboratory findings, medical history, and response to therapy into a composite picture of the patient in your mind.

This technique of examination and follow-up is the process of "thinking like a doctor." You are becoming a physician only to the degree that this form of thinking begins to make sense to you, and to become a part of your everyday thought processes.

Case Presentations, Clinical Conferences, and Grand Rounds

While your daily work on the ward, informal as it may seem, is part of learning to be a doctor, other more formal teaching exercises also will train you to think as a doctor thinks.

We have said before that doctors do not stop learning
medicine when they finish medical school and internship. Besides their reading in medical journals, physicians constantly
participate in other forms of medical learning. Three of the
most common ways doctors keep themselves alert and
learning as doctors are through case presentations, clinical
pathological conferences, and grand rounds. As a medical
student in the third year you will learn to participate in all
three.

You will frequently gather with your classmates in small
groups for "case presentations." Here an experienced physician will select a patient with whom you are not acquainted
and "present him to the group," that is, review the patient's
history, the physical findings and laboratory findings. You
may be asked to present a patient whom you have worked
up. Then, after the patient is dismissed, the possible diagnoses are discussed. The differential diagnosis may be listed
on a blackboard while the group discusses ways that certain
of the diagnostic possibilities may be eliminated or confirmed.

There is seldom any formal organization to these presentations. You do not study tuberculosis one week and kidney
disease the next. Instead, you study whatever cases are present on the wards. Sooner or later, through your experience,
you will come in contact with many different kinds of illness,
so that formal organization isn't necessary.

This apparently haphazard approach to clinical medicine
disturbs many medical students. They are afraid they will
miss something important because a case never comes to the
hospital. Suppose, you think, that I never see a case of Raynaud's disease? (You have been reading about Raynaud's
disease and are worrying about recognizing it.)

The answer is: Perhaps you never will. It doesn't matter
too much. In this "haphazard" way of learning medicine you
will see most often the diseases which are most common. You
will seldom—perhaps never—see the diseases that seldom
occur.

When I was a third-year student the disease known as
"disseminated lupus erythematosus" was a class favorite. Everybody was eager to see a case. I never did see it in medical

school, although I read about it and heard it discussed frequently. But during my internship year I saw five cases of lupus, including one in which I was the one who made the diagnosis.

This illustrates another basic principle of medical education: You do not learn all there is to learn, or see all there is to see, during your years in medical school. You may practice medicine for fifty years and see something new in a patient every day. But you do learn to apply what you have learned from your experience, from textbooks and journals, so that when the patient with disseminated lupus erythematosus does walk into your office ten years from now you examine him, take his history, stroke your chin, and think to yourself, "Hmmmm—wonder if this might just possibly be lupus?"

Or—more likely—you miss it completely and one of your colleagues picks it up right under your nose, leaving you with a red face. Fine. You can live with a red face—but at least you will be sure of one thing. You won't miss the next case of lupus that comes along.

This is how you learn medicine.

Another way doctors learn is in clinical-pathological conference. Here the case presented is a patient who has died in the hospital, or has been to surgery where a definite diagnosis has been established. Everyone present tries to determine from the history, physical findings, and course in the hospital exactly what was wrong with the patient. The differential diagnosis is listed, but now there is a difference. The pathologist (remember him?) knows the answer. He has tissue sections to prove it. Sometimes someone hits the diagnosis on the head, but frequently no one comes near the truth.

Usually these cases are extremely difficult ones—the "problem cases" that have puzzled the most experienced physicians in the group. By learning in this way, where mistakes have been made, you will learn how similar mistakes can be avoided in the future.

Grand rounds is the most formal exercise you will participate in as a medical student. Here the chief of a service will make formal rounds on his wards, picking the cases he thinks are the most instructive to discuss. If the chief of service is a good teacher—as he usually is—grand rounds offers you an excellent opportunity to benefit from the experience of a skilled physician.

The Surgical Service

Another section of your third-year time will be spent in surgery.

Often there is rivalry between the medical service and the surgical service in a hospital. At the University Hospital in Philadelphia we were informed, on our first day of surgical service, that we would "walk a little faster, work a little harder, and practice a little better grade of medicine" than on the medical service.

Certainly we walked faster and worked harder. In most cases surgical patients come to the hospital with a specific problem which can be relieved, or improved, by surgery. They may not be sick at all otherwise. Consequently, the admission work-ups are more concerned with the "surgical lesion" than with the patient's general state of health.

The number of patients assigned to you will be much larger than on the medical service. Each patient's care will fall into three categories: preoperative work-up, surgery, and postoperative care.

As an extern on surgical service you will be expected to work up patients entering the hospital one day for surgery the next. Often they arrive on the evening before surgery, which means you will be working late into the evening completing your preoperative work.

You will be expected to "scrub" on many of your cases. Naturally you will not be given very critical assignments in the operating rooms. You will learn why surgical retractors are known throughout the profession as "idiot sticks"; nothing is quite so difficult as standing for hours holding retractors in exactly the right position, especially when your hand and wrist begin to cramp and your foot goes to sleep. You will think that a hook on the wall could do the job just as well and not get nearly so tired. But you will observe operations of many different kinds.

You will also learn all the careful procedures that go into

maintaining a clean operating room and a sterile surgical
field. A certain amount of your time is spent working with the
anesthetists, learning to administer various types of anesthet-
ics.

Certainly you will not have much experience as a surgeon
in surgery. Your job is not to learn to do surgical operations.
Surgeons spend from three to five years after their internships
learning that. As a medical student your major concern will
be surgical diagnosis, learning to recognize the various types
of surgical lesions and surgical diseases. You will be expected
to learn how to treat burns, infections, fractures.

Even more important, you will learn about the post-opera-
tive care of patients, to help them recover from their "surgical
wounds" and get back to normal life as quickly as possible. In
the hospital emergency room you will learn to see many patients rapidly, to come to conclusions about their problems, to
deal with them on the spot if possible or to admit them to the
hospital if necessary.

You may not like your work in the operating room. To
some students it is the breath of life: they are the ones who
will ultimately become surgical residents and surgeons. Other
students hate it. But, like it or not, you will almost certainly
develop a deep and lasting respect for the surgeon and what
he can do.

Surgeons are occasionally unpleasant people to be around.
Irritable, brusque, conceited, arrogant, narrow—these are
some of the milder words used to describe certain surgeons,
and perhaps with some justification. But in no place in medicine are the pressures and demands on an individual greater
than upon the surgeon in the operating room. He has a great
deal to cope with, and his relations with other physicians
often suffer as a result.

The medical student on the surgical service often feels that
he is on the bottom of a very heavy pyramid. He is the one
who does the "uninteresting" work while others higher up
have the fun. Some students allow themselves to become so
miserable on surgery that they miss 90 per cent of what is
waiting there for them to learn. This is unfortunate, for there
is much to be learned. You will have to learn it somewhere if
you are going to be a good doctor. Less concern for your

personal feelings and more for the work at hand will pay
dividends here.

The "Minor" Services

Actually it is unfair to speak of pediatrics, obstetrics, psychiatry, or public health as "minor services," for they are no
more "minor" than is any other aspect of medicine. Nevertheless, they do not consume as much of the student's time, and
they are overshadowed by the great all-inclusive services of
medicine and surgery.

Pediatrics, according to the medical dictionary, is "that
branch of medicine which treats of the child and its development and care and of the diseases of children and their treatment."

At first glance this may seem to be even more of an
artificial distinction than the one made between "medicine"
and "surgery." The truth is that pediatrics deserves a separate
class even more than the others. Many doctors make the great
mistake of dealing with children as though they were "small
adults." Nothing could be further from the case.

In pediatrics the doctor is always more concerned with
health than with sickness. Children are hardy creatures. With
reasonable protection and care they will come through most
illnesses with flying colors. However, when a child gets sick
he can get very sick very rapidly. He cannot be treated successfully as a "small adult" because he just isn't a "small
adult."

On pediatric service you will become acquainted with the
diseases and abnormalities which occur most commonly in
children. Many of these conditions may occur in adults also,
but they are primarily children's diseases. But much more of
your time will be spent learning how to help keep a healthy
child healthy.

On the wards you must learn a special technique of physical examination, for a child will not sit quietly by and allow
you to examine him as an adult might. You are working with
a patient who is, to all practical purposes, deaf-mute; a child
either cannot or will not tell you where he hurts, or how his
illness began.

Pediatrics embraces both medicine and surgery. It is for the different techniques of diagnosis and treatment, as well as for the unique group of ailments, that you will spend time on a pediatrics ward.

Your experience in *obstetrics*, the care of pregnant women from the onset of pregnancy through delivery of the child, will be confined to work in labor room and delivery room during your third year. You probably will not perform any deliveries yourself, but you will assist at many deliveries. In the labor room you will follow patients through the dramatic series of events that occur from the onset of prebirth activity, which we call "labor," right through delivery and care of both mother and child after delivery. You will learn how medications can be used to ease the patient's discomfort during labor without endangering either mother or child. You will have an opportunity to observe a number of the rare but critically dangerous complications of pregnancy and labor, and to see what is done to diagnose and correct them. Perhaps you will assist at Caesarean sections, and see when and why a Caesarean should be performed.

Obstetrics has its joys and its sorrows. Your "patients" are not really patients at all; they are young women in the prime of health, about to engage in one of the most wonderful and joyful of all human experiences: the birth of a child. Unfortunately, however, women having babies have no control over the clock, and they have no regard for the sleeping hours of their doctors. On obstetrics you will be expected to live on the labor floor, on twenty-four-hour call. You may get little or no sleep, and what you get will be in bits and snatches. You will spend hours by the bedside of a single patient in labor, only to have her deliver during the ten minutes when you ran down to the cafeteria for a sandwich. Sometimes during rush periods it will seem that the whole world is descending around your ears.

But you will learn a great deal about pregnancy, and labor, and delivery.

As with many other things in your third year, you will get as much out of your service on obstetrics as you choose. If you feel like rolling over and going back to sleep when you are notified that a delivery is imminent, chances are that nobody will care one way or the other. You are not bearing the responsibility—yet. All you miss is what you might have learned.

But you can stand the rigors of twenty-four-hour-a-day call for a brief period of time without any danger to your health. The more you see and assist with in your third year the better prepared you will be when you *are* bearing the responsibility later on.

In *psychiatry* most medical schools send their students to a state or county mental hospital for a period of time in the third year, so that they may observe firsthand the care and treatment of patients with mental and emotional illnesses.

This is a far cry from the practice of psychiatry as it is popularly pictured, complete with fancy office, couch, and diploma from Vienna. Mental illness has many manifestations, some of them shockingly strange. Your job now is to learn diagnosis rather than treatment. The only way to gain real insight into mental illness, what it can do to patients and how it can be dealt with, is to spend time in a mental hospital.

The pace here may be slower than elsewhere in your third year. There will be many conferences. Psychiatric histories are long and detailed; psychiatric examinations often are extremely complex, taking hours or even days to complete. Your time on the psychiatric service in the third year will be devoted more to understanding the problems than to figuring out what to do about them.

Much the same may be said for *public health and preventive medicine.* Through field trips you will become acquainted with the various federal, state, and local agencies that exist in every community for dealing with problems of health that affect all the citizens. These are services which the citizens pay for, and which every physician will use in his practice. The better he understands their use and purpose the better equipped he will be as a doctor.

The Literature

Not all your third-year work will be in the hospital. There will be lectures every day on clinical medicine, surgery, pediatrics, obstetrics, psychiatry, and many of the subspecialty fields of medicine such as ophthalmology and neurology. What free time you have will be spent on your textbooks, for in third year your reading is almost as important as your ward work.

You will become acquainted with certain medical journals, too. More and more in hallway debates and "curbstone consultations" you will hear doctors referring to "the literature." To a doctor "the literature" means the many medical and scientific journals which report new work being done in laboratories and hospitals all over the country.

In the medical library you will learn to track down specific articles about specific subjects, discovering which journals are useful to you and which are not.

Above all, you will read and read. Now, in the third year, you will begin to feel the pressure of time as you have never felt it before—a harbinger of things to come, for this pressure will never relax throughout your professional career. You will want to read far more than you have time for. Here the fast, comprehensive reader has a great advantage over his slow-reading colleagues. If you did work in corrective reading during college, and did not allow yourself to slip back into your old sloppy reading habits in the meantime, you will reap your reward now and from now on.

Certainly as you finish your third year of medical school you will feel that a great change has come about: You started as a medical student, and now you are a doctor. Perhaps an incomplete doctor, with little confidence in your abilities and even less experience, but you are a doctor nonetheless. The fourth year still lies between you and that coveted diploma, but already you know what being a doctor feels like.

It's a wonderful feeling.

ELEVEN

Medical School:
The Fourth Year

THERE IS SOMETHING very special about the senior year in any kind of school, and medical school is no exception.

Once more you have climbed up the ladder a rung at a time and now the view from the top is a little dizzying. It's hard to say just what the difference is. You approach this year's work with a different sort of anticipation, and with more confidence than you've felt all through medical school.

You realize that for months now you haven't given a serious thought to whether you would pass or fail. You have gradually recovered from that odd feeling that comes when you are called "doctor" in the hospital or in recitation classes. It begins to sound and feel natural as you start your work this year.

Chances are that you've had a busy medical summer prior to returning for your fourth-year work. Many medical schools want their students to have a period of practical medical work away from the atmosphere of hospital and lecture hall, and require that you spend the summer between the third and fourth years in some form of medical endeavor.

Some students spend this time working with a private physician in practice, seeing patients with him in his office and making his hospital rounds and house calls with him. Others take jobs in public health agencies or mental hospitals, working in a professional capacity as doctors. Still others spend the time in research projects.

Such a summer can offer you an excellent opportunity to investigate the possible fields of medicine you may want to choose from. Already you are looking beyond medical school. You are thinking of internship and wondering which field of medicine will best fit your interests and abilities.

Perhaps you already know what you want to do in medicine, but most likely you will still be undecided. The summer of clinical work will give you the chance to try one thing or another on for size. You may discover, after a summer's work with a general practitioner, that general practice is for you the most fascinating and challenging way to practice medicine—or you may be disappointed by its limitations, and decide that a specialty field would suit you better. The summer's work will help you decide.

Also, it will help you develop confidence in yourself as a physician, an important matter as you start your fourth-year work.

Whatever you do the summer before, chances are that you will have a good case of the "fourth-year jitters" by the time September rolls around.

Quite suddenly, one day, you realize that your formal medical training is almost over. Of course you still have nine months to go, but they will pass swiftly. What's more, they will be spent primarily in the outpatient clinics, seeing many patients briefly, with little of the close and lengthy follow-up you had with your inpatients. You will spend time catching up on some of the relatively minor specialty fields. You will not be working in the wards or operating room very much. You have already had as much experience with hospitalized patients as you are going to have before internship stares you in the face.

It is a bit frightening, for you don't feel that you are ready for internship yet and you don't see how this final year will make you feel any more ready for it. You feel a little like the baby bird that is about to be pushed out of the nest and told to fly, whether he's ready to fly or not.

So perhaps this is a good time to stop a moment and take stock of the broad viewpoint once again—to consider what you have already accomplished in your preparation for medicine.

What do you have to know to be a doctor? Many, many things, as you now know from experience.

But how can you tell when you know enough?

Foolish question, because you now know that you will never "know enough."

You have spent years in college exploring many fields of knowledge, growing up and maturing, developing the habits of study you would need in the tougher grind ahead. Through all those years of preparation you were studying medicine.

You spent two years in medical school learning the scientific basis for medicine—the whys and hows. You carefully built up the scientific groundwork upon which you will be building for the rest of your life.

You have spent a single year—a tremendously rich and exciting year—learning to apply that scientific groundwork in diagnosing and treating patients, learning the art of medicine.

Now, in the year to come you will reinforce what you have already learned, seeing patients as a practicing physician would see patients, learning to think clearly and judge wisely.

No part of it was unimportant, and no part was complete. In the last analysis, the study of medicine is not what you learn, nor how much you learn, nor how well you learn it, nor when you learn it. The learning in itself does not make you a doctor, nor give you the right to be a doctor.

The thing which makes you a doctor is the change that has taken place in yourself throughout these years of study, to make you the kind of man or woman who can use what you have learned with honesty and humility and sincerity to help the people who will be putting their faith and trust in you—your patients.

If this process of change and growth had not taken place, all the knowledge in the world could never make you a doctor. But the very fact that you are concerned whether you could possibly know enough or not is proof that the change has come about.

The Outpatient Clinics

In many ways your fourth year is pleasantly different. There is less pressure upon you, more time for reading, for contemplation, for thinking medical problems through, and for exploring new and interesting facets of medicine.

Your days will be spent in the outpatient clinics of the hospital, seeing patients in much the same way that a physician would see them in his office.

You will listen to their problems, examine them, plan studies and treatment for them, and follow them on their return visits, under the careful supervision and assistance of experienced physicians, your preceptors.

In some clinics, such as medical clinic, you may follow the same patients throughout the year, helping them to find the solutions to their medical problems. To these patients you become very much their doctor. They look to you for advice, and they trust in your judgment.

One patient I had been seeing in medical clinic had a long history of trouble with his duodenal ulcer. At one time he had had a severe hemorrhage from the ulcer, but had recovered without surgical intervention. When he came to medical clinic we worked together hoping to control the ulcer by medical means until it had time to heal completely.

We talked about ulcers, and why people had them, and how to take care of them while they were healing. I prescribed his medications, saw that he followed the program we had set up, and checked his progress periodically with X rays. Each step was carefully discussed with my preceptor, who was following the patient with as much interest as I was.

One weekend my patient began hemorrhaging from the ulcer again, and was brought to the hospital by ambulance, in shock. A gastrointestinal surgeon known throughout the country was called to see the man; his verdict was inevitable. The patient needed surgery, and quickly, to stop the bleeding. To wait would be to risk his life.

But the patient refused to sign permission for surgery. Instead, he asked to see me.

When I reached his room he was very weak and frightened. He asked me if I thought he ought to have the surgery. I told him I thought it was the only thing to do.

"Will you be there at the operation?" he asked me.

I promised him I would. Only then would he sign the permit and allow himself to be taken to the operating room.

I was not a graduate physician, I was a fourth-year medical student, and the patient knew that. But to him I had become his doctor, and he trusted my judgment when he would trust no one else's.

This was not an unusual occurrence in the fourth year. It happened to many students. Whenever it happened it drove home the degree to which a patient places his faith and trust in the hands of his doctor. This was just a foretaste of what the practice of medicine is like when medical school and internship are far behind.

In the surgical clinic you will have the opportunity of long-term follow-up of postoperative patients. You will follow patients who have had surgery for cancer, examining them for evidences of recurrence and rejoicing with them when no evidence appears. In pediatric clinic you will consult with mothers and their babies in "well-child conferences" in which you will prescribe formulas, give inoculations, and otherwise help the mothers safeguard their new babies' health.

You will learn specialized techniques of examination in ophthalmology and otolaryngology clinics. In the psychiatric outpatient department you will gain greater insight into emotional disturbances, and assist in carrying patients in psychotherapy, working with skilled psychiatrists.

There will be some inpatient work yet. Some time will be spent on the gynecology service, dealing with the diseases of women and assisting with gynecological surgery. You will return to the labor room again, but this time you will have the opportunity to perform deliveries yourself with the assistance of obstetrical preceptors.

Finally, you will have more time to read, in both textbooks and journals. Fourth year is a time for tying up loose ends; it is the time when you establish more strongly the admittedly shaky foothold you have obtained in the science and art of medical practice.

March 15: Looking Toward the Next Year

In your fourth year you will be concerned with your impending internship.

Once again you must make application for admission, secure

letters of recommendation, and appear for interviews. But things are not quite the same as they were four years ago. Now you are applying for internships, and there are more internships by far than there are prospective interns to fill them.

Of course certain internships are more desirable than others; in fine, well-known teaching hospitals there is often stiff competition for an internship. But much more likely you will find that the hospitals are competing for you!

It is a strangely welcome feeling.

In recent years the problem of fitting prospective interns into suitable internships has been all but solved by the National Internship Matching Plan. Under the plan the fourth-year medical student applies to the hospitals in which he would like to serve as intern, and lists them according to choice. Each hospital in the plan surveys the number of men who have applied there and lists the men by choice. The lists are matched, and the prospective intern is automatically placed in the hospital highest on his list of choices that will accept him.

Thus March 15—the day all matching-plan internships are announced—has become a day of excitement for fourth-year students. You may not get your first-choice hospital, but you will probably get at least your second or third choice. Even those students who are not matched still can obtain excellent internships, for many fine hospitals do not obtain the number of interns they need through the matching plan, and immediately begin contacting unmatched students.

From March until June of the senior year—the dog days of medical school—is a long wait. Final examinations are taken in those schools which require them of fourth-year students (many schools do not). Finally the day of reckoning arrives.

Graduation exercises are solemn, but somehow you can't quite get the feeling that you are graduating from anything into anything; you have been a doctor all this year, and you will be a doctor next year, and the next. Still, you wear the cap and gown with extra pride, for now the hood bears the dark-green velvet lacing of the Doctor of Medicine. As the exercises proceed you hear the Oath of Hippocrates read, binding you to the vow of service and selflessness to which physicians have given their word and bound themselves for thousands of years.

Finally you receive the diploma, and you know your years of formal medical training are at an end.

Now you are indeed a doctor in name. It remains for you to make yourself a doctor in fact.

The Problem of Money

I have passed by certain of the problems that arise in the course of medical school in order to present an unbroken account of progress from first year through graduation. Two of these problems deserve attention because they will affect a large number of students sometime during medical school. These are the problems of money and marriage.

It is obvious from the foregoing chapters that a medical student has very little free time for part-time work to help pay his expenses in medical school.

Unfortunately, expenses in medical school are high. Tuitions vary over a wide range, but very few schools charge less than four hundred dollars a year even to residents of a state attending a state-supported school. Average annual tuition is from five hundred to one thousand dollars per year, depending on the school and the residence of the student, and some schools have tuition fees as high as fourteen hundred dollars a year.

Besides his microscope and the various diagnostic instruments he must have, such as a stethoscope (inexpensive) and an ophthalmoscope (quite expensive), the student has an annual expense for textbooks approaching one hundred and fifty dollars a year. He must have a place to live close to the university and hospital. He must have money with which to eat.

In addition, the medical student does need to play from time to time, and should have a reasonable amount of money in his budget for dates, movies, sporting events, etc. To the medical student "recreation" comes very close to the literal meaning of the word. He needs a break from his studies periodically, if only to gain a refreshed outlook on the world outside his own little absorbing world of medicine.

Where does all that money come from?

If your family can pay your bills either as a gift or as a loan, fine, but this can be quite a burden on a family.

You can't count on earning more than a fraction of the money you will need while you are in medical school. You simply don't have the time. You can't make the time.

Furthermore, medical schools that have scholarships available almost always reserve them for upper-class students who are in need of funds to finish their training. The first-year student, at least, must look elsewhere.

One source of assistance in the first year may be members of your family outside of your immediate family group, and family friends. Often aunts and uncles will be happy to help with expenses on the basis of a loan. Perhaps a married brother, unable to offer regular financial support, could finance your microscope. A cousin might provide a year's book money.

There is no reason in the world to be ashamed to ask to borrow money from anyone who might be able to lend it to provide funds for medical school. The fact that you have been accepted by a medical school is something to be proud of; if you need money to capitalize on your opportunity, why be ashamed of that?

Also, you have the summer between college and medical school to lay in a cash reserve. Granted that summer work is not always high paying, even a little saved will help.

One student I knew requested Christmas gifts of cash. He knew that he wouldn't really need the shirt ($4.95) that Aunt Mabel would send him after racking her brain trying to think what he might like nor did he need the adventure novel ($3.50) his brother would buy for him and which he would not have time to read. He requested the money instead, and used it for what he really did need: three months' room rent.

Once the first year is behind you, fund raising may be less of a problem. A man who has successfully completed a year of medical school has proven that he has the stuff to make the grade and become a doctor. Odds are good that he will be able to go ahead and finish. For him, a number of sources of funds become available if he needs help to pay his way.

Many colleges and universities have their own private loan

funds to aid students with cash loans that can be carried for several years at very low interest. In addition to such restricted sources of funds, certain national organizations award scholarships or outright cash grants to outstanding students, and many state and county medical societies endow scholarship funds for promising students from their areas. In 1961 the Association of American Medical Colleges published an up-to-date pamphlet entitled, "Sources of Information on Financial Aid to Medical Students." Copies of this pamphlet may be obtained free of charge by writing to Dr. Ward Darley, Executive Director, Association of American Medical Colleges, 2530 Ridge Avenue, Evanston, Illinois.

Until very recently, however, funds from such sources either have been available only to the rare and outstanding student, restricted to residents of specific areas (or students of specific medical schools) or reserved as emergency funds to aid students who might otherwise have been forced to drop out of medical training in midstream. The average medical student of limited means—especially the first-year student—often found himself facing all-but-insurmountable problems in trying to finance his medical school expenses. Too often the cost of training alone would discourage promising but penniless students from even considering careers in medicine. They just couldn't see any hope of footing the bill, and the profession was losing thousands of fine prospective doctors to other careers on this account.

Clearly something needed to be done; in 1960 the American Medical Association Education and Research Foundation (AMAERF) came up with a revolutionary answer to the problem. It seemed ridiculous . . . and grossly unfair . . . that worthy and promising students should be barred from medical training solely for lack of funds, especially considering that these same students, once through their training and practicing medicine, could count upon better-than-average incomes and would be considered excellent credit risks by any standards. Money lent to them to pay their education costs would be collectible, with interest, five or ten years later with practically no risk of default. Banks had been aware of this for some time, and certain banks had lent money to medical students on just such a rationale as this with only life insurance as security. The Education and Research Foundation went a step further and began gathering money together to serve as security for bank loans to medical students on a massive scale.

Early in 1962 the AMAERF Medical Education Loan Guarantee Program was formally launched By the end of 1962 it was already a resounding success. Over $515,000 had been donated to the Guarantee Fund by American physicians all over the country; an additional $460,000 had been given by pharmaceutical companies and other private industries. This money itself was not to be lent. Rather, it was deposited as collateral for over $6,000,000 in loans made to medical trainees in 1962 by private banking organizations at a favorable interest rate and with no additional security. Every $100 in the Guarantee Fund could secure up to $1,250 of loan money . . . enough for tuition and books for a full year for one medical student somewhere. The only strings attached were that the student borrowing through the program be a citizen of the United States and be enrolled in an accredited medical school, internship or hospital residency program. Loans were available to first year medical students and fourth-year surgical residents alike, regardless of their prior financial status.

The AMAERF program is truly a major break-through in solving the problem of financing medical education. With such an enthusiastic reception in the first year, efforts have been extended to enlarge the Guarantee Fund; in July 1963 it had increased to a total of $1,340,000. By the time you are beginning your medical school training it seems certain that the AMAERF program will be a major source of funds for physicians-in-training in all walks of life. Many doctor think of the program simply as an example of a great profession rallying to take care of its own. But more than that, it means the removal, once and for all, of the financial barrier that has blocked so many promising young people from pursuing the road to medicine. It means that any student, regardless of means, can stand on his own feet and meet the cost of his own medical training privately and in an honorable way, without any need to resort to government support with the inevitable taxation and political control that would soon follow.

Of course it would be unfair to enter medical school expecting to call upon emergency funds to pay your way (although it *is* comforting to know that they can come to your aid in a pinch). Borrowing through private channels such as the AMAERF program, however, is something else altogether. Under the present program a student may borrow as much as $1,500 each year beginning with his first year of medical school, up to a maximum of $10,000 over a seven-year period throughout his medical training. The total number of students who can be assisted is limited only by the size of the guarantee fund; within a few years as much as $50,000,000 is expected to be available through the program, enough to provide 33,000 loans of $1,500 each or one $1,500 loan to each of 5,500 doctors-in-training every year! Repayment is deferred until the student has completed his medical training, and then loans can be repaid over a period of ten years if desired. Further information can be obtained from the office of the dean of any medical school, or direct from the American Medical Association Education and Research Foundation, 535 North Dearborn Street, Chicago 10, Illinois.

Perhaps the program's best feature is that it offers premedical students of limited means a sound basis for planning to meet the expenses of their future medical educations. Of course, such a program implies a period of private indebtedness when training is completed . . . but so does a mortgage on a house. Borrowing money is a time-honored way to finance any venture, particularly a venture as worthwhile as your training as a doctor. You aren't asking favors when you borrow for this purpose, nor are you asking for "something for nothing" since you expect to repay with interest.

However, even maximum aid through the AMAERF program will not pay all your expenses in medical training. You may have to explore many avenues to raise funds, and you may not exactly live like a king while you are in medical school. But nobody will worry if your collars are frayed as long as they are clean.

You will not be the only one in medical school who is low on funds!

The Problem of Marriage

The question of marriage while in medical school is a sticky one, especially since we seem to be in the midst of a great change of attitude toward it.

A generation ago students were seriously advised against marriage until their training was finished. Those were the days of the handsome, young, unmarried interns; fewer than 10 per cent of graduating medical seniors were married at time of graduation.

Five years ago it was not surprising to find as many as 80 per cent of the seniors in a class married by graduation time; today it is estimated that 80 per cent of *all* medical students are married, and the hospital nurses have to look far and wide for an unmarried intern. Obviously things have been changing.

Veterans returning from World War II were older than their prewar counterparts, and many brought wives and children back to campus with them. These men proved beyond question that merely being married did not have the adverse effect on classwork that it once was thought to have. On the contrary, the extra measure of maturity and incentive these students brought to college with them led to better-than-average work. Their unmarried colleagues had to work extra hard just to keep up with "those damned average-raisers."

The same thing has proved true in medical school. Nine years after high school is a long time to wait for marriage; it might be twelve or fifteen if residency were counted in. More and more families feel it is right to "help out" to get young married couples started financially. Furthermore, the modern American girl is no longer so interested in having a thirty-five-year-old bridegroom hand her the world on a silver platter. She wants to marry him at twenty-five and help work for the platter!

Almost all medical-school wives work full or part time to help pay the bills and get their husbands through medical school. Budgets are often slender, and many a student has beaten a path to the dean's door in his third or fourth year with a familiar tale to tell: Everything had been fine financially as long as his wife worked, but now she was suddenly and unaccountably pregnant and couldn't work any more. . . .

But they managed to get along just the same.

It's up to every student thinking of marriage to realize that marriage is a job in itself, which requires time and patience and good will and money. These things will have to come from somewhere, and they can come at the expense of studies. Many students believe that the advantages make up for the loss, but medical-school marriages unquestionably must carry an unusual burden of strain. There were two divorces in my class during the four years of medical school, both directly the result of the extreme demands that medical school made upon the men involved.

Students should realize that studying can be difficult enough by itself without having a baby crying all evening and half the night in the close quarters of a two-room apartment.

Any girl who marries a doctor must face the fact that she will have to share her husband with a demanding profession. His work will come first, whether it means missed meals and midnight hours or not. If she doesn't want that she had better not marry a doctor. But if she knows it and accepts it, she will have an early initiation by marrying a man in medical school. She will see her husband disappear into the hospital for days at a time during his internship. And she can be sure that residency and practice will not be very different.

The odd thing is that there seem to be lots of girls who don't mind at all.

For Girls Only

Throughout this book I have said a great deal about the gamble the would-be doctor must take, and the odds he faces as he starts along the road to medicine. Because there is, and always has been, a preponderance of men in all phases of medical training in this country, most of my remarks have been directed at male medical students; it might seem that I have been deliberately ignoring the fact that every year more and more girls are becoming interested in careers in medicine.

Actually, most of the information in this book is just as applicable to women who want to be doctors as to anyone else. Certainly a girl must face all the problems a man must face in approaching training in medicine. She must have precisely the same premedical background, the same medical school courses and the same internship training. But in addition, she will have to cope with certain special problems a man need never even think about. What is facing a girl who wants to be a doctor? What special considerations should she have in mind when she makes her decision to go into medicine, and what special barriers will stand in her way? Does a girl really have a chance, or would she be wise to forget the whole idea and look to some other field of interest altogether?

The answer is that it depends entirely upon the girl.

There is no question that women can be just as good doctors as men. This has been proven time and again. Nor are women in medicine any particular novelty; there have been women doctors practicing medicine throughout history, and in recent years most of the old traditional barriers against women in the profession in this country have finally been breaking down. Yet even today a girl faces an uphill battle to win acceptance in a medical school, and she may well have to endure an attitude of vague disapproval and patronage on the part of her male colleagues as long as she remains active in medical practice.

In part, this attitude toward women in medicine is ridiculous and selfish. The men just don't like to see their beloved, traditionally male profession (which in many ways resembles a vast exclusive fraternity) being invaded by a crowd of women. Even when the profession as a whole began to accept women in the ranks more readily, many groups and organizations within the profession have remained adamant. A girl still has a tough time obtaining a really good surgical residency in the United States, and a still tougher time passing surgical specialty board examinations, for instance.

But there is more involved in this prejudice against women than selfishness. Even the most progressive medical school thinks twice about admitting a female student, for perfectly valid reasons. Any girl interested in medicine should consider these reasons most carefully before making her decision. A man who completes his medical training is likely to be actively engaged in some aspect of practice or other medical activity for the rest of a long and productive life. A woman is far less likely to do so. While marriage and the raising of a family do not interfere in the least with a man's pursuit of a medical career, many a woman doctor discovers that she simply cannot do both and do justice to either. Though she may start out with the firmest intentions of practicing even after she is married, she finds that home-making and family-raising is a full time job in itself. When the children come the practice goes, and her use of her medical training, to all intents and purposes, is at an end.

Of course, this is not invariably the case. Certain exceptional women do succeed in combining two careers—wife and mother on the one hand, practicing physician on the other. Especially in these days of group medical practices or office partnerships, with effective sharing of night and weekend call responsibilities, a woman doctor can hope to work out an arrangement to maintain at least some medical activity if she marries and children arrive.

The trouble is that no one—least of all yourself—can predict in advance just what your own capabilities may be. In our society, a woman's first responsibility is to her home and children. But a doctor's first responsibility is to his (or her) patients. If you are contemplating a career in medicine, you should fully realize that you may later be faced with a painful choice between practice and family—especially if you discover that you just can't do as much at the same time as you thought you could.

Certainly a girl who wants to be a doctor has a chance—statistically almost as good a chance as a man. But the girl who approaches medicine with the idea that somehow she can find a way to eat her cake and have it too will very probably find herself in trouble sooner or later. If your basic ambition is sometime to marry, make a home and raise a family, you should give careful consideration to alternative (and less demanding) careers than medicine. On the other hand, if you want to be a doctor more than anything else and have the determination and perseverance to travel the long road, just being a girl will not make as much difference as you might think. You can expect the medical school admission committee to be more critical of your application than they would of a man's; they will want to be quite satisfied that you will really use your medical education once you have it. And there will always be certain of your colleagues in medical school and beyond who will refuse to take you seriously as a doctor. Like it or not, you will always be a woman in a man's world —but ultimately, if you are a good doctor, you will win the respect of your brothers in medicine wherever you go.

TWELVE

Internship and Upward

YOU ARE A Doctor of Medicine, and you are starting your internship.

I would have to write another book twice as long as this to begin to tell you what your internship year will be like. I'm not even going to try to do so in this one. It will be enough to say that you are at the bottom of the ladder again. Your internship year is primarily a year of service to your profession—but it is far more than a year of work in a hospital.

This "fifth year of medical school" will be the most difficult of all. It will also be the richest for you, because in medicine you learn by doing, and during your internship you do.

This is the year when you put into practice the long period of training you have just completed. As a house physician in a hospital you will be the first to see the patients who are admitted there. You will record the history and physical examination on each patient admitted. You will assume personal responsibility for the patient's well-being and progress during his stay at the hospital, working closely with his private physician or with your ward chief. But now you will be working as a colleague in medicine, not as a medical student.

Often you will have first crack at diagnosing the patient's illness and will write the initial orders on his chart to start him on the way to recovery. You will be the first to observe any changes that come about, and the first to observe the patient's progress.

More than that—you are the house doctor. When something goes wrong, you will be called first. When additional orders are indicated, you will be expected to write them. You will live in or very near the hospital, and on your duty nights and weekends you will be "covering" large numbers of patients.

In addition to admission work-ups on new patients and your own regular business rounds you will make rounds with staff physicians, assisting them in whatever way you can in the diagnosis, care, and treatment of the patients. When spinal punctures are to be done, you will do them. When a thoracentesis is indicated, you are the man responsible for it. When a woman suddenly goes into shock three hours after her baby has been delivered, you will be the one the nurses call. When a patient expires, you are elected to tell the waiting family and to secure permission for post-mortem examination.

Much of your work will be the endless series of little details and decisions which make a hospital run smoothly. You will work closely with residents and staff doctors. You will assist at hundreds of surgical operations. You will perform many deliveries and assist at many more.

You will learn, the hard way, that the practice of medicine goes on night and day, every day, and you will never stop running from July 1 to the following June 30. But you will learn more medicine in your internship year than in all the previous eight years put together.

How much or how little you will be allowed to do will depend upon you. No one is going to drop major responsibility into your lap the first day. As the weeks go by you will gradually learn the ropes. Many very practical things were never touched upon in medical school. You will learn what steps to take, in what order, when a patient is brought to the hospital at four in the morning with an acute coronary thrombosis. You will learn what to do for a patient in shock. You will learn to diagnose by diagnosing, and blundering, and learning, and diagnosing again.

You will not have much time to read, but you will absorb medicine through every pore. You will make mistakes, and sometimes patients will die because of the mistakes you have made. This happens to every doctor; you must learn what it is to have it happen before you are ready to be a doctor yourself. On the other hand you will make diagnoses that others have missed, and do exactly the right thing at the right time, and save the lives of patients who would have died except for your judgment. This also happens to every doctor, and helps a little to take the edge off the mistakes he has made in the past and will make in the future.

No doctor knows all there is to know. No doctor's judgment is infallible, nor even approaches infallibility. In your internship year you are merely storing up a bit more of the knowledge you will need in the practice of medicine.

You will realize more than ever why you must never stop learning.

The year will go quickly as you rotate through the services in a now familiar pattern: medicine, surgery, obstetrics and gynecology, pediatrics. You will go to conferences discussing the patients whom you have seen and worked up. You will hear physicians with forty years of medical experience admitting that they don't know what to do, and perhaps accepting the ideas of a resident physician of one year's experience as the best possible answer.

It lasts only a year. Where you go from there is up to you.

More and more, with the growing complexity of medicine, young doctors want more training before starting practice, and stay on as hospital residents after internship. Sometimes they stay only for an additional year, if they expect to enter general practice. For specialty training in medicine, surgery, or other fields they may enter a full residency program of three to five years.

Whatever your choice, the doors are wide open. Practice, training for a specialty, research, teaching—the choice is yours. You have invested nine years and thousands of dollars in an education and way of life. What you do with it is up to you.

You may be certain of one thing, however. No matter what field of medicine you enter, there is work to be done. There are new roads to be explored. There will always be a place for you in medicine wherever you go.

You can be sure that whatever you and medicine do together you will never be bored with each other.

Index